What You
Should Know About
SUBMARINE WARFARE

What You Should Know About
SUBMARINE WARFARE

DAVID O. WOODBURY

Drawings by Louis H. Ruyl
Diagrams by the Author

W. W. NORTON & COMPANY, INC.
PUBLISHERS NEW YORK

This book was originally published under the title
WHAT THE CITIZEN SHOULD KNOW
ABOUT SUBMARINE WARFARE

PRINTED IN THE UNITED STATES OF AMERICA
FOR THE PUBLISHERS BY THE VAIL-BALLOU PRESS, INC.

TO THE FIGHTING AMERICANS

WHO DIED BECAUSE THEIR WEAPONS WERE

"TOO LITTLE AND TOO LATE"

CONTENTS

LIST OF ILLUSTRATIONS

ACKNOWLEDGMENTS

To APPROACH the subject of submarine warfare candidly at this crucial time, it has been necessary to plot a course midway between saying too little and revealing too much. In this risky piece of navigation I have had the hearty co-operation of the United States Navy and particularly of the United States Submarine School at New London, Connecticut, to whose officers and enlisted men I am grateful for many hours of patient demonstration and explanation.

The Navy's public-relations men have also smoothed my way into many active sources of information not easily accessible in time of war. They have done this in the belief that the American citizen will participate more intelligently in the great conflict if he is in possession of all facts which do not actually aid the enemy. Those facts are carefully gathered here for all to consider well. They explain, I believe, why the submarine is the deadliest menace of 1942 and at the same time indicate how it will eventually be overcome.

When Mr. Hitler's spies buy him the book, as they undoubtedly will, it may give him, too, a glimpse of the handwriting on the wall. I hope so, anyway. It would be a pleasure indeed to help win the war by adding even minutely to the burden the Führer is already carrying.

Especially am I indebted to Paul Shubert, a former naval officer of many years' experience, for his kindly and careful scrutiny of the manuscript and his seasoned technical advice. And I am grateful to Nat A. Barrows, whose book, *Blow All Ballast,* has given me the flavor of the submarine background.

On my own behalf let me add only this: In the research for *Submarine Warfare* I learned for the first time that during the four months I spent with the Atlantic Fleet in 1918 I was in constant danger of being torpedoed by a German submarine. I had felt a trifle ashamed of accepting the soldier's bonus. I don't any more.

DAVID O. WOODBURY

Tuckahoe, New York

FOREWORD

More than six million tons of merchant shipping went down by U-boat attack in World War I. How many vessels have succumbed so far in War II only the highest officials know. But it is certain that the unabated sinkings of today constitute the greatest present threat to Allied victory. In the desperate struggle to rid the earth of Hitler and his gangs, ships are the key. The purpose of this book is to show how ships are sunk and how they may be saved.

The submarine is the Jekyll and Hyde of naval warfare. It may be used in honorable battle against other fighting ships, or it may be perverted to as sordid a form of gangsterism as ever was used on land. In its infancy the undersea boat was as unappreciated as any other world-shaking invention. Naval authorities were too conservative to believe in it and too unimaginative to fear it. But when the Germans introduced modern piracy in 1914 the submarine suddenly became the greatest military innovation since gunpowder. In a few months it had made long-accepted naval strategy obsolescent, and by 1918 had changed the theory of war itself.

President Roosevelt has termed the U-boats the "rattlesnakes of the Atlantic," but that is a gross libel upon a reptile that never strikes unless attacked, and then never without warning. Submarine warfare in the German mode is cowardly, inhuman, and desperate—a thoroughgoing perversion of the high naval tradition of Lord Nelson and John Paul Jones. But that fact is of no help to us now. Like the rat, we must exterminate this sneaking enemy by the swiftest and most ruthless means available.

Of itself the submarine is as beautiful a piece of mechanism as human ingenuity ever devised. Essentially, it is a solo instrument with which its commander is free to garnish his record with atrocity or sublime courage, whichever suits his conscience best. In civilized hands, confined strictly to military uses, it is not the rat but the Commando of the seas, and its crew often rise to great heights of self-sacrifice. The sub's story is a continual paradox: a strange mixture of mechanics and mischief, of endurance and degradation. It becomes intelligible only when we review its history in the light of the double life which it has been forced to live.

The Allies beat the U-boat in World War I by sheer overwhelming numbers—of cargo ships, patrol craft, and depth charges. They won because their opponents had waited too long to press home the advantage submarine warfare had given them. However, though temporarily defeated, the U-boat was already the victor in the opening battle of the future conflict; it had spawned a principle more dangerous than itself; it had shown the way to total war, without rules, without warning, without honor or tradition.

FIGURE 1. *Heading West for America*

Far-seeing military men in every country realized the danger ahead. But these men were too few to be heard. So comfortable were the victors in their "peace without victory" that they did not sense the terrible urge for revenge which smoldered in the Teutonic soul. They did not see that this peace was but an armistice in disguise, which must yield eventually to a second phase of the struggle, more deadly than the first. Amazingly, they did not reason that the weapon with which Germany had nearly split the British Empire would inevitably be used again.

Everything that has followed, everything that we are involved in today, is a direct result of the blindness and lack of realism in which the democracies have persisted without a break since 1919. There would have been no Battle of the Atlantic, no throttling of commerce on our own coast if we had maintained even that degree of submarine defense which ended the last war. Because we did not so prepare we are still on the defensive today, after three years of new struggle on the high seas. Until we are strong again—stronger than ever before—that struggle will see no end.

It is my purpose now to trace the submarine from its historic beginnings to the present, and to show how this drab little orphan of the world's navies became, in an incredibly short time, the greatest weapon of deceit ever invented—a weapon for which there is as yet no satisfactory answer.

CHAPTER ONE

THE SUBMARINE EMERGES FROM HISTORY

BIRTH OF THE IDEA

LIKE the modern steam turbine the submarine had its origin with the early Greeks, but it failed to mature for two thousand years because it was not needed. At the Siege of Tyre in 332 B.C., Aristotle records, soldiers clad in diving dress were sent down to chop holes in the bottoms of Alexander's ships. He says that air was supplied to them through tubes whose open ends were floated on the surface. A crude form of diving bell was also used, the sage believes, but he gives no hint that either scheme had practical results. Pliny mentions early diving operations that were equally vague. All were presumably stunts such as Archimedes' plan to set fire to the Roman ships at Syracuse by means of mirrors flashing the sun's rays from the city's walls.

Travel under the sea had the same romantic hold on man's imagination as flying through the air, but for many intervening centuries it remained a paper dream. In the sixteenth century Oalus Magnus, Bishop of Upsala, recorded the use of leather boats that could go below—the first authentic mention of submarines.

In 1573 William Bourne, chief naval gunner to Queen Elizabeth, wrote a treatise entitled "Inuentions or Deuises very necessary for all Generalles and Captaines, or Leaders of Men, as well by Sea as by Land," suggesting methods by which the Spanish Armada might easily be overcome. Bourne's "18 Deuise" was "a Ship or Boate that may goe vnder the water vnto the bottome, and so come up againe at your pleasure." This ingenious craft was to be constructed with strong wooden framing covered by a watertight skin of leather. Screw jacks within were to distend or contract the sides and thus alter the displacement, causing the ship to sink or rise at will. For ventilation Bourne suggested a hollow mast protruding above the water. What use was to be made of this first genuine submarine the author did not say. It was never built; the British Navy dealt with Spain successfully in the conventional manner.

Imaginative submarines persisted after that for centuries. As late as 1822 Captain Montgery of the French Navy proposed an underwater dreadnaught to be called "L'Invisible." She was to carry four underwater cannons, eight carronades, one hundred torpedoes, one hundred rockets, and a ram. Not satisfied with all this, Montgery added a force pump with which to scuttle his victims. The grandiloquent scheme quickly disappeared into the archives of the French Admiralty and was never considered again.

In 1869 a romancer proposed a submarine—this time Jules Verne with his famous *Nautilus,* in which

Captain Nemo traveled 20,000 leagues under the sea. The vessel went far ahead even of present-day design, for it was propelled by an ideal electric motor that needed no storage batteries, and had large plate-glass windows for observing the fish. Even William Beebe in his bathysphere has had to get along without this convenience, staring through a tiny deadlight barely big enough for one pair of eyes. The modern sub has no windows at all except the telltale periscope, which is often its undoing.

EARLY CRAFT

PRACTICAL submarine experiments, however, began in the seventeenth century in the reign of King James I. About 1624 Cornelius van Drebel, a Dutch engineer serving in the Royal Navy, built a submersible and launched it into the Thames. It was a careful embodiment of William Bourne's earlier plan, and actually cruised for two hours at a depth of fifteen feet, making the passage from Westminster to Greenwich —several miles—without mishap.

Van Drebel solved the problem of breathing air simply by making his sub large enough to contain several hours' supply. For propulsion he used oars protruding through flexible leather seals in the sides of the ship. This extraordinary craft did not founder even after repeated trials, and it became so celebrated that King James himself finally made a dive in it.

Nothing was done, however, to add such vessels to the navy, for at that time no one saw how they could be used.

Soon afterward a Frenchman, de Son, visualized a submarine for military purposes, and in 1653 he built a small one to prove his contention. It was interesting mainly because it disclosed the first use of paddle-wheel propulsion on any vessel. De Son fitted his wheel in the center of the craft with the lower part in contact with the water. He made it revolve by hand. After successful tests of this submersible warship the inventor offered to "destroy in one day a fleet of one hundred vessels." He claimed it would travel at ten miles an hour and believed he could make a round trip to the East Indies in ten weeks. Both boasts went unheeded. De Son was put down as a fool.

An interesting romantic at this period was John Wilkins, Bishop of Chester, who published a "Discourse concerning the Possibility of a Passage to the World in the Moon," and many other fantastic propositions. He became so popular that his works ran into many editions. In one brochure he suggested "an Ark for Submarine Navigation, for use against a Navy of Enemies, who by this means may be undermined in the water and blown up." He was thus the first to see how a submarine could be made effective.

Bishop Wilkins's greatest contribution was the use of water ballast to increase the sub's weight and cause submersion. He also suggested that breathing air might be kept fresh by condensing the "evil humors" out of it against the cold sides of the ship. These novelties, like many before them, remained untried, though they contained the kernel of future success.

BUSHNELL AND FULTON

A HUNDRED years passed without appreciable advance, and then the submarine was suddenly christened as a vessel of war in the American Revolution. In 1776 the patriot, David Bushnell, built his famous *Turtle* for the purpose of attaching mines to the bottoms of British men-of-war. Bushnell figured that his sub would take the British by surprise, and, if successful, maybe win the war. Being a Yankee from Connecticut he was determined to try out the scheme himself.

The *Turtle* was very small, constructed of oak planks in the shape of an egg on end, with the operator in the position of the yolk. A hand-turned corkscrew affair edged her along at one mile an hour; lead ballast kept her upright; a valve in the bottom let in water for submerging and a hand force pump got it out again for coming up. Bushnell found that he could stay down half an hour before the air got too foul to breathe. For surface travel he devised ventilators which closed automatically when the water struck them.

Attached to a latch on the outside, Bushnell carried a 150-pound canister of gunpowder with a time fuse. The canister was connected by a rope to an auger bit protruding vertically through the top of the vessel. A crank inside allowed the inventor to screw the bit into the bottom of the enemy ship so that the bomb could be affixed to it. The plan was to approach the victim quietly at night, submerge and set the explosive, then slip away to await results at a safe distance.

When the time came for an actual attack Bushnell

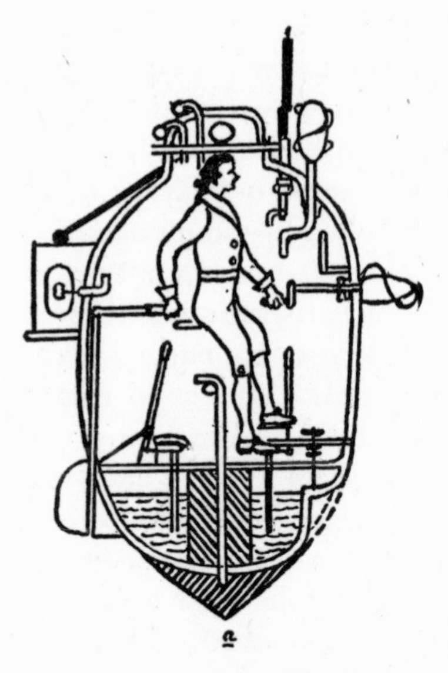

FIGURE 2. *The* Turtle

decided to delegate the adventure to a soldier named Lee who was eager to try his hand. Accordingly, one dark night, Lee proceeded down the Hudson River to the British frigate *Eagle,* anchored off the Battery. The bomb was ready with the fuse already set. Bushnell waited impatiently on the shore.

Nothing happened for a time. Then the harbor was

shaken by a terrible explosion at some distance from the intended victim. Lee had made contact with the ship and had worked nearly half an hour before he discovered that she was copper-sheathed and could not be drilled. In a panic lest the time fuse should set the bomb off under him, he had detached it and had fled at the *Turtle's* top speed.

There was great excitement in the British fleet, and a heavy watch was set against further mysterious explosions. Lee tried several times more but was unable to get into position for the clumsy operation of drilling his hole. Discouraged, Bushnell gave up the attempt and returned to Connecticut. Twenty years later, he went to Paris, hoping to sell his invention to the Directory for use against the English fleet. Making no impression at all, he retired to America and gave up submarines for good.

In Paris with Bushnell in 1797 was young Robert Fulton, a discouraged artist who was trying to interest Napoleon in ship canals. Bushnell's idea caught his imagination, and he decided to stay on and succeed where the older man had failed. Immediately, he drew up plans for a submarine to be called the *Nautilus,* and presented them to the Directory. The politicians declined to take them seriously. Fulton waited patiently until a new Minister of Marine was appointed, then submitted his plans again, pointing out that submarines could destroy the English Navy and leave France the mistress of Europe.

The new official was friendly and made a favorable report on the invention. But the Directory again ignored it. Fulton went to Holland with his proposition but was turned down there. Back in Paris he made a third unsuccessful attempt to interest the politicians, and finally, in 1800, built the *Nautilus* with his own money. The vessel was of wooden frame construction covered with iron plates and sheathed with copper. It was hand-driven by a propeller having

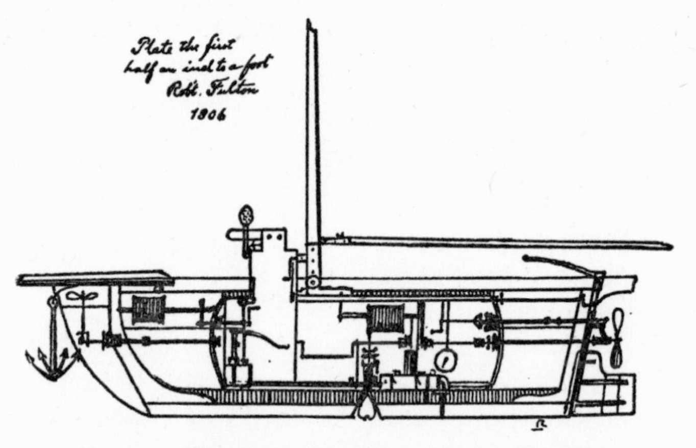

FIGURE 3. *Fulton's Own Plan for the* Nautilus

four separate blades, instead of the inefficient corkscrew form of his predecessors. This was one of Fulton's great contributions to future marine engineering.

After a preliminary test in the Seine, Fulton took the *Nautilus* to Le Havre and remained submerged in the harbor there for six hours, obtaining air through a tube with its open end floating on the surface. Elated with this triumph he submitted a report to Napoleon, promising him world dominion if he would adopt the submarine. The Emperor made no reply; but Fulton, carried away by his own enthusiasm, swallowed the slight and kept on. Within a year he had rebuilt the *Nautilus* with many improvements, among them an explosive mine which could be hauled against the bottom of an enemy ship by a cable running over a winch within the submarine. Still more important was a spherical tank of compressed air from which the interior of the boat was replenished from time to time. In many respects the new *Nautilus* was the true forerunner of the modern submarine.

Test runs at Brest proved highly successful, and Fulton devoted himself to the work exclusively for the next four years. During all this time the French authorities showed great interest, though no inclination to purchase the idea. At one time Fulton offered to attack a British frigate lying at Brest and blow it up. But the Maritime Prefect refused permission. "This manner of making war against an enemy," he cried, "carries the adverse criticism that a person using the device and sinking with it would be lost. Certainly that is not a death for military men." An ironic contrast with the principles of modern war!

Eventually Fulton heard that Napoleon had characterized him as a charlatan and an adventurer and that he would do nothing about the *Nautilus*. The Emperor was already the dictator of half of Europe and was on his way to conquer the rest. Disillusioned, Fulton now turned against the French, and in 1803 opened negotiations in London, where he received the warm support of Prime Minister William Pitt. Contracts were eventually signed with the British Navy and for three years Fulton acted as a naval consultant, receiving in all £13,000. A new experimental *Nautilus* was built and Fulton demonstrated it, together with his underwater mine, by blowing up the brig *Dorothea* in the Thames.

Pitt stood by his young protégé in the endless negotiations which followed, but he was powerless against the brass-bound conservatism of the Admiralty. Six days after the successful sinking of the *Dorothea* Admiral Nelson had won his immortal victory at Trafalgar, and the British Navy decided that submarines would forever be unnecessary. First Sea Lord Earl St. Vincent summed it up thus: "Pitt is the greatest fool in creation to encourage a mode of war which those who command the sea do not want and which, if successful, would deprive them of it."

By 1806 Fulton had accepted defeat and had returned to America. He had already written two letters to President Jefferson recommending the submarine, but had had no reply. So now he gave up the idea and began to work on the steamboat, which later lifted him to immortal fame. In 1815 he tried again to build a submarine, to be called the *Mute,* a giant eighty feet long, designed to carry a hundred men. But while it was still on the ways he died, and the remarkable boat was left to rot where it stood. Thus ended in failure the work of the real father of the submarine warship, buried and defeated by the hidebound conservatism of fighting men.

THE SUB GOES TO WAR

NEVERTHELESS, the submarine itself would not be downed. In 1815, a professional smuggler named Johnson is said to have built a submersible and to have run contraband into the United States with great success—thus anticipating by just 101 years the famous trips of the *Deutschland* through the British blockade to Baltimore and Boston. So successful, indeed, were Johnson's trips that he went to Paris and laid before Napoleon's secret agents there a proposition for rescuing the Emperor from St. Helena. The scheme looked good to these desperate men, and Johnson was guaranteed £40,000 to build his submarine. His price, if successful, was to be £80,000 more. But Napoleon died before the expedition was ready to sail.

For the next fifty years many foolhardy men played with the submarine idea, but none succeeded. Cerva, a Spaniard, was killed outright on his first descent. A Dr. Petit of Amiens made spectacular demonstrations, but ended with the same fate. In 1851, an American shoemaker named Phillips built a stanch little craft which worked so well in Lake Michigan that he took his wife and two children out for a ride. Unwisely, he went too deep; neither the family nor the sub ever came up. Presumably their little boat was crushed by the hydrostatic pressure below.

The most persistent advocate of the naval submarine was a Bavarian named Bauer who built a thirty-five-ton boat called the *Brandtaucher* at Kiel in 1850. It was soon lost in a dive, and though the inventor escaped, the German government refused him funds for further work on the ground that the submarine was too dangerous a weapon. "If successful," they said, "it will render all surface navigation impossible." The Austrians agreed. And they were right. Twice since, the German Navy, most reluctant in the world to adopt the sub, has nearly overcome the world with it.

After the fashion of military inventors, Bauer began peddling his vessel through Europe, and at one time enjoyed the hearty support of Albert, Prince Consort of England. But the first sub he built sank with a large loss of life and put an end to the royal enthusiasm. The Crimean War was raging at the time and Bauer hurried to St. Petersburg and advanced his idea there. Money was forthcoming, and he built for the Russian Navy the *Diable Marin,* a truly formidable craft with a number of ingenious devices. She was fifty-two feet long, with a twelve-foot beam, and was driven by a screw propeller worked by the foot power of the crew. In the bow end were two rubber diaphragms through which a man could pass his arms to the water outside without causing a leak. A keg of powder was attached to the hull near by, to be released against the enemy ship, and a glass deadlight gave the crew a full view of the delicate operation.

When the sub was finished, Bauer gave a demonstration by penetrating secretly into the Kronstadt Naval Base on the Baltic, and he caused such a bad scare that vessel and inventor were almost annihilated by the marine guards. But Russian officialdom was typically reluctant with its approval, and the Crimea was at peace long before the *Diable Marin* could be put into service. Bauer eventually had a quarrel with the authorities and died in 1875 penniless and discouraged. But it would have heartened him to know how apprehensively the European governments looked

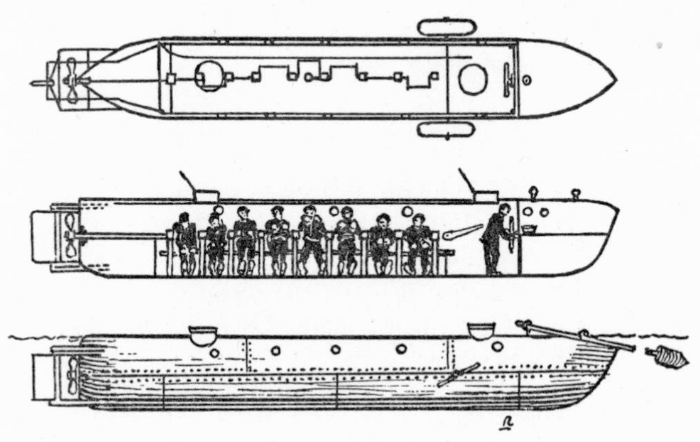

FIGURE 4. *The* David

back on his successes. All of them wished they had had the foresight to take up his invention while he was still alive.

Meanwhile the desperate Confederate government in America had made hasty experiments in undersea craft. A sub, most appropriately named the *David,* was built to attack the Goliaths invading southern ports. The *David* was of boiler iron and carried nine men who turned the propeller shaft by hand. A mine protruded from the bow at the end of a spar. This was supposed to go off on contact.

From the first this vessel played in hard luck. During her trials she sank five times and lost five crews. The sixth trial was a mission of destruction into Charleston harbor. Admiral Porter's *Naval History of the Civil War* gives this account of the affair:

"On the 17th of February, 1864, the fine new Federal vessel *Housatonic,* 1264 tons, lay outside the bar in Charleston harbor. At 8:45 P. M., Acting Master Crosby discovered something about 100 yards away which looked like a plank moving directly towards his ship. All the officers of the squadron had been officially informed of the fact that the Confederates had constructed a number of diving boats and were planning mischief against the Northern navy. When, therefore, the officer of the deck aboard the *Housatonic* saw this object approaching, he instantly ordered the anchor chain slipped, the engines backed and all hands called on deck. It was too late. In less than two minutes the infernal machine was alongside. A torpedo struck the vessel just forward of the mainmast in direct line with the magazine. A terrific explosion took place and the *Housatonic* rose in the water as if lifted by an earthquake, heeled to port and sank at once, stern foremost. The crew, who most fortunately had reached the deck, took to the rigging and were soon rescued by boats from the *Canandaigua,* which lay not far off. The *David* was afterwards found fast in the hole made by her own torpedo. She had been sucked in by the rush of water which filled the sinking wreck. Her crew of nine were dead."

The Confederacy was so elated by this success that it built a number of other submarines, naming them all *David*. During the last year of the war these progenitors of the U-boat were claimed to have sunk thirty-four Union ships in all.

The Civil War actually marked the birth of the practical military submarine. Naval authorities were wakening to its possibilities. In 1866, the United States Government contracted with O. S. Halstead of Newark, New Jersey, for a small sub which the inventor called the *Intelligent Whale*. She carried ten men and was operated by hand by a screw propeller. Halstead very nearly lost his life in the trials, and the Navy condemned her and refused to make payment. She rests on the lawn at the Brooklyn Navy Yard today, an interesting relic, the first submarine ever contracted for by our government.

THE FIRST MODERN SUBS

ADOPTION of underwater craft was slow because there was no good way to propel them submerged; human muscles were plainly inadequate, and the only other prime mover, the steam engine, was too cumbersome with its boilers, open fires, and huge demand for combustion air. Nevertheless the answer was close at hand. The world was just entering a tremendous period of invention in the electrical and mechanical fields. Thomas Edison and Professor Elihu Thomson were soon to develop electric motors and generators of commercial value. Fauré and Planté in France had just invented the lead storage battery. The internal-combustion engine was about to appear in crude form and gradually progress toward the efficient diesel. It remained only for engineering talent to apply these discoveries to submarine warfare. In America, the work was done simultaneously by two men—John P. Holland and Simon Lake. A typical penniless inventor, Lake plugged along alone; Holland had money and official backing in Washington. But the modern submarine embodies the genius of both.

In 1875, Holland built a tiny craft sixteen feet long and only two feet in girth. Its propeller was turned by foot power. It had no significance except that it carried torpedoes which could be towed behind and set off by electricity. His second sub was larger and was the first to be run by a gasoline engine, both on the surface and below. But the danger from carbon-monoxide poisoning proved so great that he would not allow the vessel to make its trials. For his third attempt Holland tried compressed air for motive power, using a reciprocating engine, but he found the operating range to be too small. This vessel was called the *Fenian Ram* and was said to have been built for the Irish to use against Britain. As a boy, Simon Lake read of these experiments and longed for the day when he would be wealthy enough to repeat them for himself.

In 1888, the navies on both sides of the Atlantic were taking the submarine seriously at last, and designs were invited. The Frenchman, de Lorne, offered the *Gymnote,* a vessel of thirty tons displacement driven by electric motors operating from storage cells.

It was pronounced a limited success, and was followed in 1893 by a 270-tonner, which also did well and led eventually to the great *Narval,* which was the French Navy's first recognized success.

Meanwhile a Swedish gunmaker named Nordenfeldt joined with an English clergyman, Garret, who had departed so far from his calling as to build a steam submarine in 1878, and the two produced the first all-steel submersible. This boat operated on the surface by steam and below by compressed air. It carried one torpedo tube in the bow, and could run for six hours underwater. It was not a great success. Nevertheless, Nordenfeldt sold it to the Greek government. Near-by Turkey bought another, and thus Nordenfeldt became a pioneer builder of submarines for the small European nations.

So far, the submersible had little more than theoretical military value—how little was shown by Germany's repeated refusal to have anything to do with it until 1906, when the diesel engine began to offer reliable propulsion. In America, Holland had not been idle. After designs had been invited by the United States Navy in 1888, he submitted plans for *Submarine No. 7,* a vessel ten feet in diameter and fifty-five feet long, with a displacement of about a hundred tons. She was to be powered with a 150-horsepower gasoline engine and with electric motors. This sub was not built till 1896, when the Navy promptly bought her and ordered another. Holland was not satisfied with the propulsion, however. The gasoline engine was neither safe, reliable, nor economical. So, in proposing his new design, the *Plunger,* he turned reluctantly to steam.

The new sub was eighty-five feet long and carried a quadruple-expansion (i. e., four-cylinder) steam engine supplied by an oil-burning, water-tube boiler which could be extinguished immediately on submersion. A seventy horsepower electric motor drove her under water. Her characteristics were excellent, her surface speed being ten knots and her submerged speed seven. She was fitted with two bow torpedo tubes and carried five small torpedoes. She was the first boat to carry horizontal bow planes with which to make a "power dive" while under way.

Meanwhile Simon Lake had constructed a tiny wooden sub and had crawled along the bottom of New York Harbor on wheels. His first real boat, the *Argonaut,* was built by the same firm in Baltimore as the *Plunger,* and the two were launched the same day. Lake was using a gasoline engine, and he very nearly killed himself and his companions on the trial run. However, the *Argonaut* lived to become a very famous vessel. In November, 1898, the inventor made a foolhardy attempt to go from the Delaware River around to New York and ran into a terrible storm. To navigate successfully he had to lash himself to the outside of the conning tower, where he remained until the little vessel made the shelter of Sandy Hook. The exploit made him world famous. Jules Verne himself cabled congratulations from Paris.

Nevertheless, the United States Navy stuck to the

Holland designs; the *Plunger* was followed in 1900 by the *Holland,* also steam-driven, and the inventor was put under contract for five more like it.

Vickers in England was then licensed under the patents, and the British built five Holland-type boats of their own. Though steam had serious drawbacks, builders were forced to put up with it until the diesel engine was made practical. The British were the first to try oil but also kept steam longer than anyone else. The *BK26,* steam-driven, was giving good service as late as World War I.

Lake thought the submarine had an important peacetime mission in salvaging sunken cargoes, and for a short time had some success in that field. With one of his early *Argonauts* he was able to recover coal from old schooners in the coastal waters, salvaging it for forty cents a ton and selling it for seven dollars. But the world had no enthusiasm for a peaceful submarine, and eventually the Lake Torpedo Boat Company was organized and began taking orders for subs from foreign governments. Lake was the man who built the *U-1* and the *U-2* for the Austrian Navy. He was also the one who shared honors with Sir Howard Grubb in England for the invention of the periscope. He sold eleven boats to Russia and came very near controlling the whole submarine situation in Europe.

Lake set out to convince Admiral von Tirpitz, commander of the Kaiser's Navy, that the sub would make a fine defensive weapon. "Ah, yes," said the Prussian, "very good. But that boat would also be good for offensive purposes. And that is what we shall want her

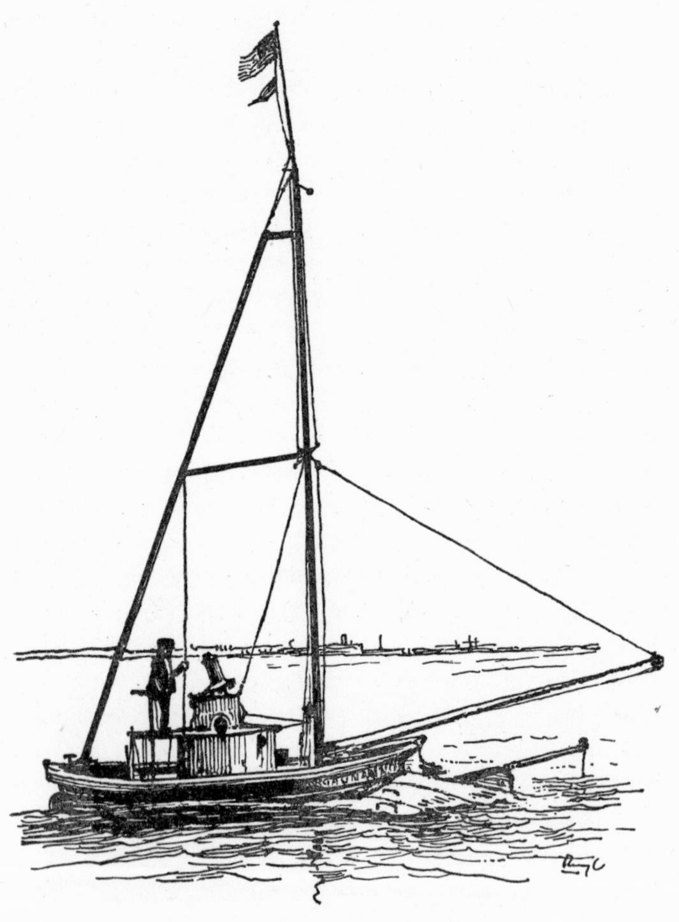

FIGURE 5. *Simon Lake's* Argonaut

for!" This was ten years before the outbreak of World War I.

Upon word from higher up, the Krupp interests instantly adopted Lake designs, and the quiet little American saw himself swept into European power politics. But German munitions makers were too smart for him; before long they had stolen his patents and had blandly pushed him out. Lake went back to America and eventually combined with the Electric Boat Company to become a major builder for the United States Navy.

In the Russo-Japanese War the submarine was still a plaything and took no part. However, in the ten years between 1904 and 1914 it was gradually adopted by all navies and was steadily improved in size and range. The outbreak of World War I found it a recognized though minor member of the naval teams. Then the Germans developed it as a commerce raider, and the heyday of underwater craft suddenly arrived. Enormous advances were made in submarine design and construction and in the efficiency of its control. The crude periscope, invented in 1902, became an optical instrument of the highest precision and the sighting device by which thousands of vessels were torpedoed and destroyed. Diesel horsepower increased tenfold as did also cruising range and the ability to stay under water. The tonnage, which had hovered around 100 or so at the turn of the century, suddenly jumped to nearly 1,000, and the slow speed, which had kept subs from being of real value in a battle fleet, increased to double and triple its old figure.

By 1918, the descendant of the little sinkable boat in which King James explored the Thames had become the most deadly of all sea-borne fighters. Alone it had very nearly destroyed the vast empire which James's successors had so laboriously put together. No longer were naval authorities cold to submarine advance; they were desperately anxious to accept every improvement that came along and especially to discover any sure means of defense against it. In the convoy system, the depth charge, and the underwater listening device they thought they had it, and so won the war. But the potentialities of the submarine had not been exhausted. Today, with tremendous inventive ability and ingenuity still at work to improve it, the undersea vessel is once again a villainous and unanswered weapon, and a challenge which must be quickly met and conquered if the United Nations are to survive.

THE INVENTION OF THE TORPEDO

THE submarine would have little significance without the torpedo, whose delivery is its principal excuse for existence. Robert Fulton gave this lethal weapon its name, taking it from a destructive marine worm that attacks the bottoms of wooden ships. The first torpedoes, invented in the mid-nineteenth century, were merely mines towed by a launch at the end of a long cable. Control wires actuated rudders which caused the missiles to veer off and strike as the enemy was approached. The Civil War brought the spar torpedo, whose success has already been noted.

In 1866, Robert Whitehead, superintendent of the naval iron works at Fiume, Austria, invented the self-propelling torpedo, which immediately rendered all previous ones obsolete. It was a complete miniature submarine in its own right, being driven with twin screws by a forty-horsepower engine operating on compressed air. It carried seventeen and a half pounds of explosive and could travel a hundred yards in a fairly straight line. It was so successful that every government in Europe began to clamor for it. Whitehead gave up all other work and became the world authority on self-propelled death. He showed such ingenuity in devising automatic controls that by the time Holland's submarine was ready for it, the torpedo could travel over a thousand yards on a steady course at about sixteen knots, and could deliver some thirty-three pounds of guncotton against the hull of an enemy.

Heavy waterline armor soon rendered this small power ineffective, and inventors everywhere set to work to make the torpedo faster and more deadly. Most prominent among them was Frank M. Leavitt, who introduced an alcohol flame to heat the compressed air, and L. Obrey of Trieste, the originator of the gyroscopic control. A steady process of refinement, including the substitution of a gas-steam turbine for the earlier reciprocating engine, has finally made the torpedo the most deadly and unanswerable attack weapon known. "When a torpedo hits anything," Admiral Hart said recently, "it stays hit."

Actually the torpedo was not invented primarily for use in submarines, but as a projectile that can be fired from any vessel, an airplane, or even a fort ashore. Its sinister virtue is that it strikes deep under the water where no vessel, not even a battleship, can afford the weight of high-resistant armor. For, witness the destruction of the *Bismarck,* the German superdreadnaught that was boasted to be unsinkable. Torpedoes fired from surface ships were the deciding factor in the Russian debacle at Port Arthur. And now, forty years later, they are still irresistible. The intended victim's only hope is to elude them or to prevent them from being fired at all.

CHAPTER TWO

THE GERMAN U-BOAT CHALLENGE: 1914-17

REGARDLESS of the doubt cast by diligent armchair apologists upon German war guilt, there is abundant historical proof that the Reich had been preparing for many years for a death struggle with England. Enormous quantities of powder and munitions were shown to prominent Americans by proud German officials in 1911. The Kaiser's Navy openly boasted its intention of surpassing the British. All the world knew then what it has forgotten now—that war was planned in Berlin twenty years before it actually came.

By the spring of 1914, the German High Seas Fleet had reached only 60 per cent of Britain's strength and was at a serious disadvantage geographically: England commanded the approaches to every German naval base and commercial harbor; she absolutely controlled the North Sea and Channel entrances. The initial problem confronting the Imperial Navy in August, 1914, was to eliminate the British fleet piecemeal, since it could not take it on a major engagement. The two attempts at this—at Heligoland Bight in 1914 and at Jutland in 1916—failed. There was nothing left to Germany but guerrilla warfare, conducted by small task forces, single raiders, and submarines.

GERMANY OPENS U-BOAT WAR

At the start the long-range value of the submarine escaped both contestants. The sub was the little country cousin of the fleet—too slow to go along with it, too short of range and too weak to venture on its own. The British Admiralty was comfortably contemptuous of the submarine threat; it had promptly mined Germany's North Sea approaches and felt secure. The Admiralty did not know that the mines were defective until it learned long after that German men-of-war were carrying them in their wardrooms as souvenirs. The Admiralty's complacence was heightened when the cruiser *Birmingham* chased and rammed the small *U-15* one week after hostilities commenced.

Berlin shared this contempt for its submarines and for the first few days sent them out from their Heligoland base only in the daytime, requiring their return by night. Von Tirpitz, Naval Secretary of State, was responsible for this timidity, for, in spite of what he had once told Lake, he regarded them as foolishly experimental. In the coming struggle with the world's greatest naval power he did not propose to waste time on untried weapons. Not till he reversed himself later did the U-boat menace begin.

Germany started the war with twenty-eight subs. Only the *U-19* to *U-28* were seagoing vessels of fair range, and these carried only two torpedoes and no guns. Their best surface speed was six and a half knots, reduced to three below. The British were little better off with thirty-eight E-boats of similar design.

When the Germans failed to enter Paris in the fall, both nations knew that it was to be a long war, and naval building programs were jumped up accordingly. Quite a few new submarines were included as a matter of course. The Germans already suspected that the little craft might be valuable, for on September 5 the *U-21* had met and sunk the scout cruiser *Pathfinder,* the first vessel in the war to be torpedoed from below. The British took painful note, and revised their haughty stand immediately. They, too, started to exploit the submarine.

Germany had instantly mined Danish waters and so had denied the Baltic to the British fleet. This left her free to move large shipments of ore down from Sweden in safety. Britain answered in October by sending *E-1* and *E-9* through the Skagerrak beneath the mine fields to prey upon Baltic shipping from a base at Helsingfors, Finland, then still belonging to Russia. The experiment proved so profitable that a large fleet of subs was kept there for three years, and was only disbanded when Russia collapsed in January, 1918. British subs were equally active in the North Sea, and early sank the cruiser *Hella.*

The Germans were likewise busy. Scarcely had the *U-21* accounted for the *Pathfinder* when the *U-9* turned in a staggering record of three enemy warships sunk in one hour. The *Aboukir, Cressy,* and *Hogue* were proceeding at high speed through the North Sea when a torpedo drilled into the *Aboukir* and sent her down in a few minutes. Her sister ships went to her rescue immediately. Otto Weddigen of the *U-9* waited till he saw through his periscope that the British were busy picking up survivors. Then he torpedoed both cruisers in rapid succession. This catastrophe cost the lives of 1,400 Englishmen, most of them on the *Cressy,* whose boats were away when the second missile struck.

This huge success gave the U-boat men a sudden impudence. After knocking down the cruiser *Hawke,* German subs got into the Firth of Forth and drove the whole Grand Fleet out to sea. The fleet sought shelter at Loch Ewe and was promptly dislodged again. At the same time the U-boats began laying mines all over English waters—mines that could not be picked up for souvenirs. For several months the Admiralty was excessively worried. The greatest fleet in the world could not find a safe place to come to anchor. This condition ended only when Scapa Flow, in the far-off Orkney Islands, was finally rendered impervious to U-boats by elaborate nets and electric mines.

The preliminary phase of the submarine war reached a climax in January, 1915, with the torpedoing of the first-line battleship *Formidable.* The fact was that the U-boat had the surface ship on the run. But the German command failed to realize it. They saw only that England was commissioning new warships faster than they could be sunk and that she was rapidly surrounding the Reich with a ring of steel that would soon strangle the German war effort at home. They believed

First Sea Lord Winston Churchill when he said: "Germany is like a man throttled with a heavy gag. . . . You know the effect of such a gag. . . . The effort wears out the heart and Germany knows it."

THE WAR ON MERCHANTMEN

THE Admiralty in Berlin was nervous and annoyed, but felt itself to be powerless. The men of the High Seas Fleet chafed at inaction. Suddenly a group of young officers proposed the unrestricted sinking of all merchant vessels en route to Great Britain. Basing their argument on the destruction of the British cargo vessel *Glitra* off Stavanger in October, they addressed von Pohl, Naval Chief of Staff, with the following demand:

"As England completely disregards international law (by its blockade on German noncombatants) there is not the least reason why we should exercise restraint. . . . We must make use of (the submarine) and do so in a way most suitable to its peculiarities. A U-boat cannot spare the crews of steamers, but must send them to the bottom with their ships. The shipping world can be warned. . . . All trade with England should cease in a short time."

This was the birth of the U-boat curse which still threatens the world. But there was strong opposition to it in Berlin. German statesmen realized the angry reaction of America to the rape of Belgium and feared to alienate her further. The Kaiser procrastinated, then reluctantly gave his permission for the war on merchant shipping. He believed he was choosing the lesser of two evils.

It was a mad scheme technically, for the U-boats were not suited to ocean warfare far from their bases. Yet they succeeded at once—so well that Berlin proclaimed to the world that on and after February 18, 1915, all British waters would be considered war zones, and that all enemy merchantmen found therein would be sunk. "Even neutral ships are exposed to danger," said the proclamation, "as in view of the misuse of neutral flags ordered by the British Government and of the accidents of naval work it cannot always be avoided to strike even neutral ships."

This statement was of profound significance for the future. Germany had repudiated the historic sanctity of noncombatants; she had enunciated the principle of total war. The contention that British ships were misusing neutral flags resulted from the Cunarder *Lusitania* sailing under American colors late in January. The United States Government had protested this practice, and was informed that American passengers had insisted upon it. The timing of the various proclamations and protests is important. Germany had begun unrestricted sinkings several weeks *before* her warning. The flag incidents were results, not causes, of her action.

Secretary of State William Jennings Bryan sent a curt note to Berlin rejecting the war-zone proclamation, stating that we would hold Germany to a "strict accountability" for American lives and ships lost through U-boat activity. Bryan did this reluctantly at President Wilson's insistence. The result was a prolonged, three-cornered wrangle on paper. Meanwhile the U-boats delightedly sank everything that swam across their periscopes.

In its own good time Berlin rejected the American rejection with the cynical suggestion that if the United States wanted to save her shipping she should provide it with naval escort. On May 1 the American vessel *Gulflight* was damaged by torpedo and her captain and two of her crew killed. Faced with a decision the President hedged, trying to arrange a compromise whereby the British blockade and the German reign of terror should cease together. The argument was lost in a maze of diplomatic exchanges. Germany went on sinking.

THE LUSITANIA *AND WHAT FOLLOWED*

THE day the *Gulflight* was attacked the *Lusitania* sailed from New York with 1,959 persons aboard. Metropolitan papers that morning had carried an advertisement signed by the German Embassy stating that "vessels flying the flag of Great Britain or of any of her allies are liable to destruction. Travelers sailing in the war zone on such ships do so at their own risk." The warning was put down as German bluster and ignored.

On May 7, about ten miles south of the Old Head of Kinsale, Ireland, while the passengers were at lunch, torpedoes crashed into the *Lusitania's* starboard side and sank her in eighteen minutes. Eleven hundred and ninety-eight people were drowned, including 124

FIGURE 6. *Torpedoing of the Liner* Anglia

American men, women, and children. Elbert Hubbard, Charles Frohman, and Alfred Vanderbilt were among those lost. Millions in America today remember the wave of horror and indignation that swept the country when giant headlines proclaimed the disaster that Friday evening. The drama was heightened by stories of extraordinary heroism and of the pitiful attempts of the six undamaged lifeboats to save nearly 2,000 people.

Germany quickly insisted that the *Lusitania* was an armed vessel carrying troops and ammunition and that she had blown herself up. The first statement was false; the second nonsense. The rifle cartridges in her hold could not have sunk a ferryboat. The most reliable account of the atrocity is contained in the findings of Justice J. M. Mayer of the Federal District Court of New York three years later, in denying damages to the survivors. The attack was premeditated and without warning, carried out by one and probably two submarines under command of Kapitan-Leutnant Schwieger in the *U-20*. At least two torpedoes had been fired, the first crippling the engine-room controls so that the ship could not be stopped. Her speed and the heavy list that developed prevented the safe launching of the boats.

Schwieger went home to become a hero, and all Germany celebrated. The city of Magdeburg struck off a commemorative medal. The Kolnische Volkzeitung crowed: "With joyful pride we contemplate this latest deed of our Navy and it will not be the last." Wilson at once composed a note so stiff that Bryan resigned rather than sign it. The President sent it anyway. Thereafter notes flew thick and fast.

In June, Germany capitulated slightly, if insultingly, by agreeing to warn large liners before sinking them. We answered that further inroads upon our rights would be regarded as "deliberately unfriendly." In August, the *Arabic* was sunk, and more Americans were drowned. In Washington, Ambassador von Bernstorff hastened to explain that the U-boat commander had disobeyed orders and that Germany disavowed his act. Later it was found that von Bernstorff invented this excuse himself. The *Lusitania* and her victims were not avenged until September, 1917, when Schwieger blundered into a British mine field off Denmark and was blown up. In the meantime the U-boats penetrated the Mediterranean and taught the Austrians how to sink on sight. It was easy pickings here, and Berlin developed the scheme of blaming all atrocities on her ally by flying Austrian flags from U-boat staffs. Austria ended the practice by threatening to remove her submarines altogether.

A year after the *Lusitania,* Washington was still embroiled in undignified and futile argument with Berlin. The extraordinary patience of the United States Government was inexorably drawing the nation toward war—but so slowly that Germany had time to build up a formidable and highly trained U-boat fleet. Mr. Wilson keynoted this patience when he said in a speech: "The example of America must be a special example. It must be the example not merely of peace because it will not fight but of peace because peace is the healing and elevating influence of the world and strife is not. There is such a thing as a man being too proud to fight. There is such a thing as a nation being so right that it does not need to convince others by force that it is right." It is a doctrine which has meant horror and death almost constantly ever since. We have only just learned that pride and righteousness do not prevail over thugs armed with such weapons as U-boats.

Wilson himself soon retreated from this lofty position. In April, 1916, he reached the point of threatening to break off diplomatic relations with Germany altogether if she did not stop sinking defenseless ships. This brought a categorical promise from Berlin, "in the interest of friendship," that vessels would not be sunk without warning and without the saving of their crews and passengers.

The U-boat campaign was now hamstrung. It was neither pursued nor repudiated. Sinkings went on, to the tune of repeated denials in Berlin. Wilson was re-elected because he had "kept us out of war." Von Tirpitz was in a mood of ugly frustration which for the moment had no effect on the ring of politicians around the Kaiser. In his *Memoirs* the old Admiral said bitterly:

"Our decision (to abandon unrestricted sinkings) freed England from the gravest material danger that it had ever known. . . . The damage that our submarines could have achieved in 1916 was far greater than that caused in 1917. Our hesitant politicians were too clever to grasp this simple truth. The yield of the submarine sank as the enemy's defensive measures increased. These measures required years of preparation, years which we gave them. The submarines could only bring us victory during a certain period and this we threw away."

Which suggests that if the United States had been as completely tough as von Tirpitz wanted to be—*soon enough*—the war might have been ended in half the time. But we compromised and kept on compromising until finally the Germans were convinced that we would never do more than talk. And Japan, fully observant, filed the lesson away for future use.

THE CRISIS OF 1917

IT IS necessary to examine the diplomatic and emotional factors of this period as well as the military exploits, because they were then, as they have been ever since, the basis for submarine warfare.

With Germany again contemptuous of American threats, unrestricted sinkings increased rapidly. On January 31, 1917, she once more proclaimed an all-out U-boat program—no holds barred, no ear open to further argument. The United States Government stiffened for battle.

During the previous months, the American ship of state had drifted toward war. A drifting vessel lies broadside to the seas; our diplomatic one was no exception. It presented a perfect target which Berlin had promptly torpedoed with words. Cynically the Kaiser's government had suggested peace. The President was

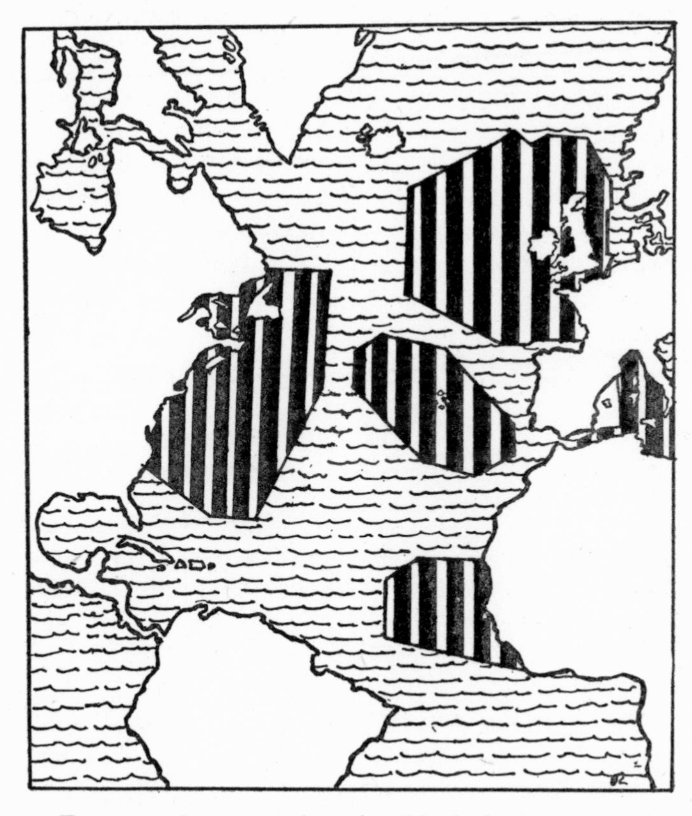

FIGURE 7. *German Submarine Blockade Zones, 1917*

receptive, and addressed a note to all the Allies inquiring as to their postwar objectives. England was enraged, and retorted with thin diplomatic courtesy that the only objective for the time being was to smash the Germans. Wilson stuck to his idealism, and as late as January 16, 1917, spoke to Congress of a "peace without victory." The British received the idea in stony silence.

This was the diplomatic backdrop against which the second act of the submarine drama would be played. The curtain was soon up. On February 2 a German note lay on the Cabinet table in the White House—a note incredibly compounded of injured innocence and arrogance. It was destined to be the prototype for scores of others in later years.

"Every day by which the war is shortened is a blessing to tortured mankind. The Imperial Government would not be able to answer before its own conscience, before the German people, and before history, if it left any means whatever untried to hasten the end of the war. The Imperial Government, if it so desires in the high sense to save humanity and not to do wrong against its own countries, must continue the battle forced upon it anew, with all its weapons. It must therefore abandon the limitations which it has imposed upon itself in the employment of its fighting weapons."

The weapons which conscience now forced upon Germany in the interest of humanity were new and terrible. One hundred and eleven long-range submarines were already at sea, and as many more were building and planned. All were armed with powerful deck guns, and many were fitted as mine layers. Crew morale was high; every man was spoiling for the chance to kill without warning.

Sinkings shot up alarmingly. British waters swarmed with unseen pirates who exultantly shelled crowded lifeboats. Armed or unarmed, the merchantman was

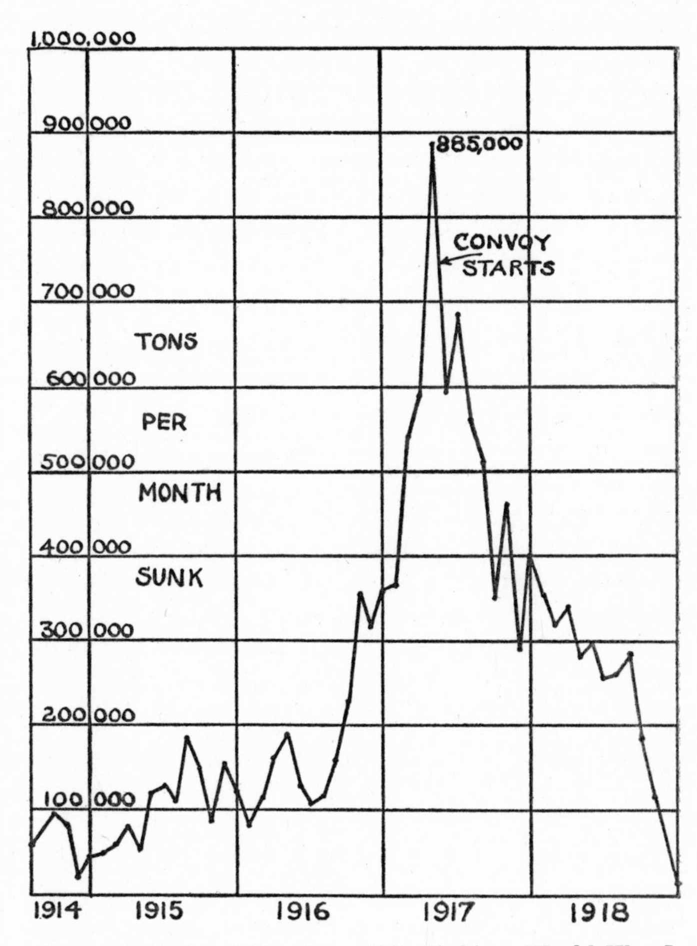

FIGURE 8. *Rate of Merchant Ship Sinking, World War I*

rare that reached harbor unmolested. So certain was submarine attack that neutrals began to keep their ships at home. Terror was overcoming the crews; worse, it was creeping over the responsible naval officers ashore, who saw that the Allied cause might soon die of strangulation.

From a "moderate" loss of 260,000 tons destroyed in January the death toll of ships soared to 880,000 tons in April. And 127,000 tons more were crippled and limped in for repairs. At one time British shipyards were glutted with 2,000,000 tons of smashed vessels. This load, on top of their commitments in new ships, swamped their facilities and ended by cutting the 1917 output to one half.

To offset this carnage the British Navy, with all its sea and air patrol and its mine barrages, in the same month of April sent only two U-boats to the bottom. According to England's foremost submarine historians: "It was a mathematical certainty that by the end of the year there would be just enough tonnage left to Britain to bring in food; nothing would be left for the transport of troops, nothing for munitions, coal or other vital necessities. Collapse faced the Allied leaders." *

The fate of England hung solely upon the next word from Washington. This was a crisis with only one solution: The U-boat must be crushed completely, not eventually but at once—a crisis well to be pondered today. Victory in the spring of 1917, as in the spring of 1942, rested upon the element of time.

* R. H. Gibson and Maurice Prendergast, *The German Submarine War,* p. 147. *See* Bibliography.

CHAPTER THREE

THE ALLIED ANSWER

A SIGNIFICANT fact came to light in that Cabinet meeting of February 2. Secretary Houston, who was present, states it as follows:

"The President asked if he should break off diplomatic relations with Germany. He immediately followed this question with a somewhat startling statement. He would say frankly that, if he felt that, in order to keep the white race or part of it strong to meet the yellow race—Japan, for instance, in alliance with Russia dominating China—it was wise to do nothing (about Germany), he would do nothing and would submit to anything and any imputation of weakness or cowardice."

Woodrow Wilson was taking the long view—too long to receive the support of his advisers. But he soon had startling confirmation in the secret Zimmermann note, intercepted on its way from Berlin to Mexico City. The German ambassador there was directed to further a plot by which Japan would attack America as soon as the United States declared war on Germany. Discovery of the scheme evidently defeated it.

But in any case the President had decided not to endure German arrogance any longer. A few days after the Cabinet meeting, relations with the Reich were ended, and Berlin's official spy, von Bernstorff, was packed off home. A short interim followed, during which the Senate filibustered against arming United States ships and won, by the action of "eleven willful men." But the country was solidly behind Wilson, and on April 6 the Congress declared war.

EARLY ANTISUBMARINE MEASURES FAILED

UP TO this time no satisfactory answer had been found to the German submarine. Diplomacy alone had exercised what little control there was. Now, merchantmen must somehow be got to and from England without being hit. Arming the ships offered no solution—Britain had been doing it for three years without success. Some entirely new scheme must be worked out. *And it must succeed at once!*

Within a few days of the war declaration, Washington and London had jointly taken up the task of mobilizing technical brains to solve the riddle. Britain well knew how indestructible the submarine was. Her own had hung up amazing records of endurance in the Dardanelles—that twenty-seven-mile-long channel swept by vicious currents and bristling with Turkish defenses. There was Lieutenant Holbrook, in the *B-11*, who lost his bearings there and came to the surface close beside the battleship *Messudiyeh*. Being unable to escape he sank her and was immediately set upon by a swarm of patrol boats. Though his compass was out of commission he dived and stayed down nine hours, underrunning five mine fields, and nearly suffocating his crew before he reached the Sea of Marmora.

The Dardanelles was a tangle of mine fields and nets. Forts lined both shores, fitted with guns and torpedo tubes. In spite of all this, the English haul in two years included two battleships, a destroyer, five gunboats, thirty steamers, nine transports, seven ammunition ships, and 188 sailing vessels. A handful of daredevils like Holbrook ended by making Turkish traffic across the Marmora next to impossible.

Similarly, the U-boats in the North Sea defied every attempt at their elimination. Again and again the British thought they had finished one, only to meet with it later in some other area. The one partially effective weapon was the mine barrage, which the British had learned to make deadly. Tens of thousands of mines were laid in the Heligoland Bight and off the Belgian coast to catch the U-boats in their lairs. These fields were responsible for nearly all the German losses before 1917.

There were also useful surface-patrol methods, notably the laying of "drifter nets." These were vast meshes of steel many miles long and some thirty fathoms deep, buoyed with glass floats. "Drifters" idled along on the surface, keeping the buoys in sight. When a sub got entangled the glass floats would be drawn under, and the patrol would pick up the net and try to force its catch to the surface, to be dispatched by gunfire. The idea failed because the tidal currents made the nets too difficult to maintain.

Still another minor weapon was the explosive sweep, towed at the end of a cable, and detonated by electricity when it fouled on a submerged U-boat. Like the nets, it failed because it was too clumsy. A variation of it, however, brought occasional results. This was a combination of a mine sweeper towing a submerged British submarine. When a U-boat attacked, the sub would creep up and torpedo her.

FIGURE 9. *The* Deutschland *Armed as a Commerce Raider*

When the United States entered the war the Admiralty had tried everything that ingenuity and desperation could suggest. All it had accomplished was to exclude the U-boats from the Channel and to force them to go north around the Orkneys to reach their Atlantic hunting ground. Germany had answered by making her submarines seagoing cruisers —1,000-tonners with ranges better than 4,000 miles. By April, 1917, she had 127 of these, and new ones coming faster than the old ones could be destroyed.

Three questions confronted the Allied board of strategy: How to keep merchantmen out of torpedo range, how to locate the U-boats, and how to destroy them. The first was the most vital question because huge shipments of supplies must be gotten through at once. The cargo vessels were nearly helpless in self-defense: deck guns, smoke bombs, escape by skillful maneuvering, all had failed. There was nothing left but convoy—the gathering of ships into fleets so well protected by warships that no submarine could successfully molest them.

CONVOY

NAVAL escort for cargo ships had been impossible to the British alone because there were not enough cruisers and destroyers available to make it work. To collect a large number of vessels in a group and then to underprotect them would have given the U-boats a priceless target. But with the United States in, the case was different. An American destroyer force was dispatched abroad at once, and Admiral Sims was sent to London as our naval chief. At home, shipyards began to rush out wooden subchasers and more destroyers. The very first convoy, crossing in May, demonstrated that the plan would work. It got through virtually intact. No longer were German commanders able to pick on helpless vessels. They were up against a fair fight at last, which was exactly what they did not want.

Organizing the convoy system was an enormous task.

To begin with, every ship on the ocean had to be located and classified as to speed and capacity, and its owners induced to co-operate. Next, routes of least danger had to be planned and sailing schedules devised to effect maximum protection with minimum escort. And, finally, skippers and crews had to be instructed in the difficult technique of sailing in crowded formation under rigid naval discipline. It was a hard lesson for the independent-minded merchant marine to learn, especially since the entire convoy had to travel at the speed of the most sluggish freighter. The Germans jeered that shipmasters would never be able to execute the intricate maneuvers demanded. Even the Admiralty had little hope—at first. But the hardy skippers rose to the occasion and accomplished the impossible.

Ashore in England a fast-working headquarters was set up to gather information, plan convoy details, and decide on ports of assembly. Sydney, Halifax, New York, Hampton Roads, Gibraltar, Sierra Leone, and Dakar were the points chosen. Regular sailing dates were designated for each, at four- and seven-day intervals, and all ships were required to depart on time or wait till the next convoy. At the Admiralty in London a vast chart of North Atlantic waters was set up and upon it were plotted, hour by hour, the positions of every U-boat reported. By radio the naval commander of each escort was given a course best calculated to avoid trouble.

At the assembly ports vessels were sorted out according to speed: those of seven knots, those of eleven, and those of thirteen or more. A single convoy included as many as thirty ships, as evenly matched as possible. It proceeded east in parallel lines roughly forming a square, with escort vessels in attendance on all sides. The larger merchantmen were armed with five-inch naval guns taken from old battleships, and provided with Navy crews. These ships were placed on the flanks. When submarines were reported near, the entire convoy went into a prearranged zigzag—so many seconds on such a heading, so many seconds on another. Zigzag patterns were changed constantly to confuse the enemy. When the danger zone had been traversed the ships dispersed to their several destinations. Going westward they assembled inshore and followed the same procedure in the reverse direction.

It was an extraordinary achievement for those merchant skippers to make. In foggy weather the ships were ordered in to half their normal spacing, each then towing a barrel or other obstruction to assist the vessel following to keep position. The captains became so skillful that convoys often zigzagged all night in total darkness and were still in formation in the morning. There were few mishaps. Occasional engine trouble dropped a ship out of line, in which case an escort fell back with her if it could be spared. Once in a while the laggards got caught, for the U-boats had been reduced to vultures devouring the stragglers. But the pickings were lean—so lean that of a total of 90,000 cargo ships under convoy only 436 were bagged —one-half of one per cent. The most remarkable achievement of all was that nearly 2,000,000 doughboys were ferried to England and France and only fifty-six men were lost. Yet a single convoy entering St. Nazaire brought as many as 31,693 men.

UNDERWATER SOUND DEVICES

ALL this would have been a failure if means had not been provided for locating and destroying the U-boats also. Since April, 1916, the British had been experimenting with a sound locator known as the *hydrophone,* in principle a doctor's stethoscope applied to the bosom of the sea to pick up the faint noises of enemy propellers. The intensity of the sound indicated the sub's distance, and by skillful maneuvering the listening patrol vessel could often be brought over it for an attack. The hydrophone's sensitivity was rapidly improved, and soon each ship carried two of them like a pair of ears, so that a directional effect was obtained. U-boats could then be located as to bearing as well as to distance, and the task of finding them was greatly simplified.

Two months before America entered the war the United States Government organized various consulting boards to pool the nation's scientific genius. One of these was the Submarine Board, composed of prominent engineers and research men from the large corporation laboratories and universities. Vacuum-tube amplifiers had just been invented, and the Board applied them to the hydrophone for an enormous gain in sensitivity. The listener was now stationed in the wheelhouse, with telephone receivers to his ears, where he could direct the patrol ship's movements in pursuit of the quarry.

When submarines closed in for an attack a number of patrol vessels deployed around them, all listening for the telltale propeller sounds. Each ship's position

FIGURE 10. *Surrender of the U-58*

was set down on a chart on the leader's bridge, and as soon as the sub was picked up its direction from each was radioed over and plotted by the patrol commander. Where the plotted lines intersected was the location of the sub. The more participating vessels there were the better, as the "fix" was thus made the more accurate. Immediately this simple geometric problem had been worked out, the patrol closed in and bracketed the enemy with underwater explosives.

The U-boat's only defense was to run for it or to lie perfectly still on the bottom if the water was shallow enough. The sub, of course, had its own hydrophones and could judge whether it had been discovered. Often it had to lie dead for hours, expecting every moment to be blasted into eternity. The sensitivity of Allied detectors eventually became so great that they could pick up the muffled clank of a German mine layer at work, and several fields were thus discovered. A hydrophone operator claimed to have heard the commander of a disabled U-boat shoot his crew one after another when escape proved impossible.

The Submarine Board made notable contributions to underwater detection, but it failed to adopt an important advance offered it, i. e., the Fessenden electromagnetic oscillator and receiver. The principle feature of this was a metallic diaphragm in contact with the sea, set into rapid vibration by a powerful generator. The sound waves could be radiated outward for several miles. If they struck the hull of a submarine, part of them would be reflected back to the sending ship. The pick-up device gave the distance to the object by measuring the time lag of the echo. A single Fessenden apparatus was thus a range and direction finder in one. It also offered an invaluable method of underwater signaling for the Allied submarines themselves.

The invention had been offered to the Navy in 1916, after many successful demonstrations, but officials had ignored it. Without the inventor's knowledge the exasperated manufacturers had then taken it to Germany (before the United States entered the war) and had promptly sold it for adoption on the U-boats. A wrong choice of wave length in the German model had fortunately cut down its efficiency, and so had robbed the enemy of an aid that might have made him invulnerable. As soon as we joined the Allies, Fessenden again offered the invention to the Navy, which now showed great interest. But the Submarine Board objected; there was the inevitable clash of personalities and obstructionism by conservatives. The men who dominated the Board preferred that new ideas come from within. Some of the authorized Navy tests of the oscillator were made in express violation of the Board's orders, which refused to review the results.

Thoroughly angry, Fessenden wrote to Edison, for whom he had once been chief engineer. Edison was also attempting to be of use to the Navy through the same tangle of consulting Boards. His reply was:

> "Fessenden. Yours received. You are not the only one who is being turned down. Up to date everything I have done has been turned down and I think this is true of all others.
>
> EDISON."

The greatest inventor of his time was working in the field of camouflage, without official result. The story is of interest now because the same situation in the last two years has had much to do with our own failure to met the submarine crisis quickly. For lack of men with a keen sense of responsibility, vital changes and improvements are ignored and major disasters, such as the scuttling of the *Normandie*, can actually occur without anyone's accepting the blame.

However, Fessenden got his reward. After the Armistice, tests in England proved his system to be some thirty times as sensitive as the best hydrophone equipment in use during the war. The outstanding point of comparison was that ships with hydrophone devices had to lie at rest in the water to eliminate the sounds of their own propellers. Fessenden's oscillator worked with the vessels underway. Hence an enormous amount of time could be saved in detecting and chasing the enemy. Oscillators are now standard equipment on all naval vessels large enough to carry them. And the celebrated British "Asdic," which has done so much toward winning the Battle of the Atlantic, is an extension of Fessenden's original invention.

One other important discovery which helped to locate the U-boats was the radio compass and direction finder, invented by two Italians, Bellini and Tosi. This was a simple loop antenna which indicated the direction from which radio signals came. At their most arrogant moment in 1917, the U-boat commanders habitually surfaced their craft at nightfall and sent radio reports back to Germany in code. The British quickly lined the coast with the new radio detectors and obtained the position of every sub in the sea. From this data, safe convoy routes were chosen while the Allied patrols began to sink subs in increasing numbers. The Germans were mystified, having no radio compasses of their own. They did not discover the trick till the war was won. Nowadays radio-direction finding is so accurate that no vessel can risk using its wireless in enemy waters. Even small receiving sets are forbidden on warships for fear that the slight feed-back from the tubes will reach the wrong ears.

EXTERMINATION

ONCE caught, the U-boat must be dealt with by explosives. Early British practice had been to sink them by ramming or gunfire, by mines or explosive sweeps. But none was really effective. The subs did not often surface, and it was virtually impossible to hit a periscope. However, in July, 1915, England first used the "depth charge," or underwater bomb dropped from the surface. It was supposed that a heavy explosion near a submarine would crush it, particularly if several could be set off on all sides of it simultaneously. A direct hit should be unnecessary.

The effectiveness of the depth charge was not proved until May, 1917, when Speiss of the *U-49* staggered back to Germany with a harrowing tale of near death from the new *wasser bombe,* which opened the ship's seams, split her pipe connections, and broke the filaments in her electric lamps. News of this got back to England, and the depth charge was instantly adopted as standard.

The weapon, known to the Americans as the "ash can," was simply a steel barrel filled with 300 pounds of TNT and fitted with a hydrostatic trigger which detonated by water pressure at a predetermined depth. The cans were rolled off the sterns of the patrol ships or lobbed through the air out of the mouths of special "Y-guns" on their decks. When a U-boat was located, several vessels laid a pattern of these deadly eggs around her. Huge columns of water were driven into the air as they exploded. If the sub was in a position

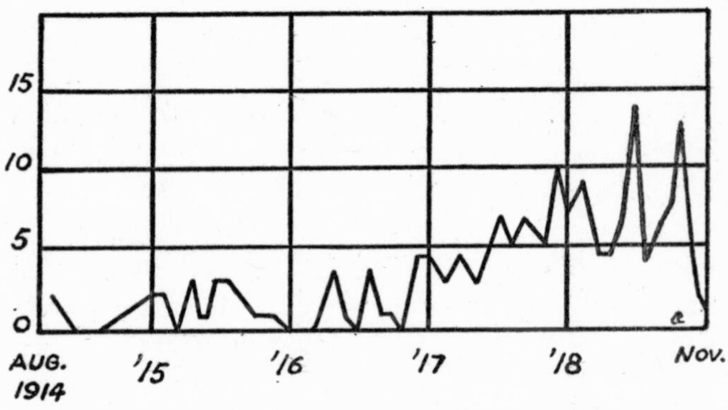

FIGURE 11. *Submarine Sinking Rate, World War I*

between or above the charges it was almost sure to be split wide open.

Depth charges were so efficient that they led to elaborate mine barrages being laid across the Dover Strait, in the Kattegat, and across the North Sea from the Orkneys to Norway. It was in these fields that the magnetic mine first made its appearance at the end of 1917. Lurking deep in the sea at the ends of their anchor cables these mines detached themselves and rose as soon as a steel hull actuated their delicate magnetic release gear. They made it impossible for a submarine to underrun the field as it had done before, for they could be planted below her safe operating depth. At that time the Germans had had no time to develop the electric degaussing cables for neutralizing a ship's magnetic attraction for the mine. This invention was not made till 1939; and since that time it has rendered the magnetic scheme useless.

By 1918, every egress from German submarine bases was closed by mine barrages. Certain narrow passageways were left in the Channel and around Scandinavia for the use of neutral shipping, and these were heavily guarded by surface patrols.

Convoy and depth charges together licked the U-boat. But the victory stemmed from the overwhelming number of escort and patrol vessels. The combined efforts of the Allied navies, plus the enormous output of their shipyards in subchasers and destroyers, were the deciding factors. The German submarine was simply smothered by explosives beneath the sea. The sole reason why the U-boats are succeeding today on our eastern seaboard is that these overwhelming numbers of patrol boats are not present.

Toward the end of the war airplanes and blimps were added to the scouting forces, and were of great value near shore. The camouflage of ships also proved useful in confusing the sub commander as to their direction and speed. There were two methods of camouflage: the low visibility or gray painting, and the dazzle. The latter was favored then, the former is in vogue now. Dazzle sought to destroy the characteristic structural forms of a vessel's hull and superstructure by painting false shadows and high lights. It made the ship more visible than before but often prevented the enemy from telling her course. Without this a torpedo cannot be fired with any certainty of making a hit. Another useful trick was to paint a white bow wave on a tramp steamer that could never produce one of her own, thus giving a false impression of her speed.

The most dramatic form of enemy deception was the "Q-boat," the Trojan Horse of the World War. U-boats could not afford to waste torpedoes on unescorted ships that could be attacked by gunfire instead. So the British devised the decoy ship, using the oldest and feeblest craft, even sailing vessels, for the purpose, stuffing them with lumber so that they could not sink. These were fitted with guns hidden behind false deck-houses or bulwarks, and they plodded along over the ocean apparently helpless. When the greedy sub commander surfaced and attacked one of these by shelling it, the little Q-boat would pluckily allow itself to be blasted till the sub was at point-blank range. Then, suddenly dropping its false work and hoisting its naval ensign, it would open up on the German and very often blow her out of the water.

These Q-boats carried the art of deception to fine dramatic extremes by holding their fire often till they were ablaze and settling. They even put "panic parties" into lifeboats and set them adrift to simulate abandoning ship. Such maneuvers fooled even the hardboiled Huns. Altogether there were 180 of these mystery ships, ranging every area where U-boats were likely to strike. Typical of their coolness and courage was the *Q-19,* which lay in wait off Gibraltar for three U-boats known to be approaching. Close to midnight the first sub appeared, and the little vessel went into her act, trying desperately to get away. All three Germans set upon her with shells, carrying away her mast and wounding eleven of her crew. The "panic party" then put off, and the U-boats closed in for the kill. Suddenly the collapsible deckhouse fell away and a 47-mm. gun opened up. The first shot knocked the senior German officer overboard. Ten more took such effect that all three subs were soon on the bottom of the Mediterranean.

END OF THE U-BOAT WAR

THE increasing danger to submarine operation made it more and more difficult to recruit good crews. There was little time to train the men and waning hope of being able to bolster their morale with promises of victory. Submarine service meant practically certain death; a kind of shell shock began to appear among those who had lived through depth-charge attacks. While there was no outright mutiny in the U-boat force as there was in the High Seas Fleet, the efficiency and spirit of sub crews were going down rapidly. Brains were slower, fingers more clumsy, discipline more lax. Significantly, the U-boats often surrendered without a fight.

One example shows the trend. In the dawn of May 12, 1918, the *U-103,* under Claus Rücker, sighted the giant *S.S.Olympic* steaming up the Channel, bulging with American troops, and escorted by four destroyers.

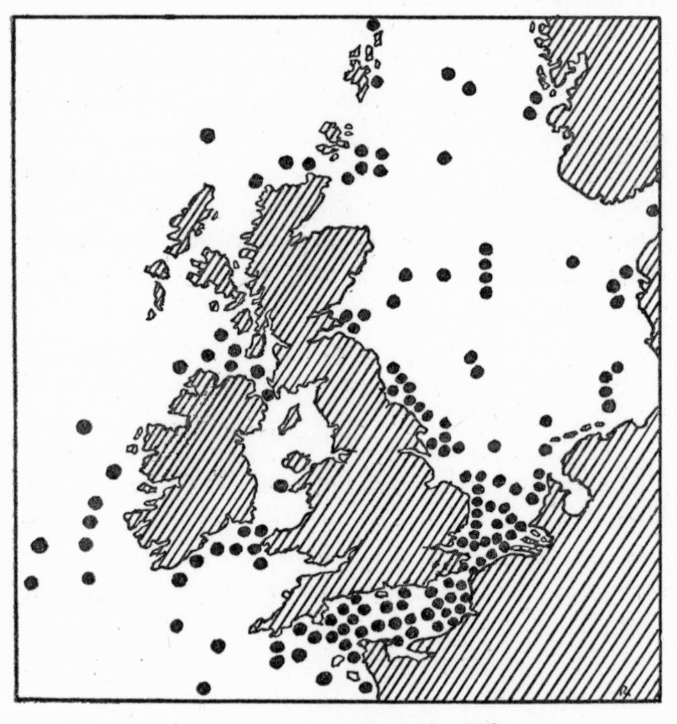

FIGURE 12. *Graveyard of the U-boats*

With great skill Rücker maneuvered into position and gave the word to his after torpedo room to fire. His men were not ready. Savagely the commander prepared to plunge deep and chase the *Olympic.* But the men at the plane controls bungled, and the U-boat surfaced. Instantly the big liner opened fire and made ready to ram; the sub tried to get away, again was not quick enough, and was nearly cut in two. Hastily Rücker surfaced his ship himself and lined up his crew on the smashed deck, crying "Kamarad!"

Especially was it difficult to find the material to make tough submarine commanders. The peculiar combination of perfect judgment, iron nerve, and the instinct for piracy had become almost unobtainable. Of the six and one-half million tons of shipping sunk by submarines, nearly two-thirds were downed by twenty-five men who averaged 160,000 tons each. The other 225 commanders averaged scarcely 12,000 tons apiece. The sinister conclusion is that if Germany had had a mere hundred more of these underwater geniuses, she would have won the war hands down. But she did not have them. Villainy was plentiful. Genius was not.

Summing up the demise of U-boat warfare, Rear Admiral William S. Sims wrote what he thought was its epitaph in his book, *Victory at Sea,* in the following words:

"In March, 1918, it became apparent that the German submarine campaign had failed. . . . Instead of being usually the pursuer the submarine was now more often the pursued. . . . It was half-heartedly lying in wait along the coasts, seeking its victims in the vessels of dispersed convoys. If it attempted to push out to sea and attack a convoy, escorting destroyers were likely to deliver one of their dangerous attacks; if it sought the shallower coastal waters a fleet of yachts, sloops and sub-chasers was constantly ready to assail it with dozens of depth charges. An attempt to pass through the Straits of Dover meant almost inevitable destruction by mines. . . . In most of the narrow passages Allied submarines lay constantly in wait with their torpedoes; a great fleet of dirigibles was always circling above, ready to rain a shower of bombs upon the underwater foe. . . . A few months later the American and British shipbuilding facilities were neutralizing the German campaign in two ways: they were not only constructing war vessels on a scale which would soon drive all the German submarines from the sea, but they were building merchant tonnage so rapidly that, in March, 1918, more new tonnage was launched than was being destroyed."

This was the antisubmarine victory as described by the American who helped achieve it. Temporary relief from U-boat pressure permitted the Allies to win the war on land. With German militarism in collapse the submarine, like all other weapons, appeared to have been wiped out. This was false optimism. The figures boded ill for any future war.

During the high tide of destruction in 1917 the Germans were wiping out $5,000,000 worth of shipping and were drowning forty men every day. By summer they had 140 U-boats in service. Then the Allies struck back. By September the submarine rolls had dropped to 127 and the monthly tonnage loss to 180,000. The bag of U-boats sunk after American entry was 132. After the Armistice 176 operating subs were surrendered and 208 unfinished hulls were broken up in the shipyards.* In four years and three months this

* *The German Submarine War, op. cit.*, p. 323 ff.

vast nest of hornets, with the mines they laid, had struck down 5,708 merchant ships totaling 11,153,000 tons. And at the moment of surrender Germany's submarine service, so far from being beaten, was preparing a supercampaign for 1919. The British have since admitted that had the war gone on into another spring, this onslaught might have won. The submarine had been controlled but not eliminated.

There were many, when the war was over, who said comfortably that the days of the submarine were past; patrol boat and depth charge would forever prevent a repetition of its threat. *If the knowledge gained in those victorious years had been acted upon, this theory would have been correct.* But it was not acted upon. It is an amazing fact that the Allied navies entered World War II swollen with the very types of ships that had been proved costly and useless against underwater attack. Presiding military genius evidently supposed that the Germans had forgotten all about the submarine and would not think to try it again.

CHAPTER FOUR

THE MODERN UNDERSEA MACHINE

In the interim between wars Germany and everybody else developed the submarine so zealously that few secrets of construction remained. What little mystery surrounded the U-boat in 1939 was quickly dissipated with the first one to be captured "alive."

During the first world conflict the British went to great risk and expense to salvage sunken German craft in order to obtain their secrets. In War II, so far, the youth and inexperience of some German crews have made such an undertaking unnecessary. Several U-boats have already surrendered on our East Coast, and these have been brought into port and thoroughly studied by our own and Allied experts. The Canadian Navy is now operating at least one ex-U-boat, and others have been captured and put into British service. If secret submarine inventions once contributed to German deadliness under the sea, they do so no longer.

The submarine is fundamentally the same everywhere. Like all other vessels its purpose is to furnish a platform from which its ordnance may be accurately used against the enemy. Relatively small space is required for the ordnance, most of the vessel being occupied by the machinery to place the boat in proper firing position and keep it there. Because so little attention is given to self-defense, every inch of space aboard can be devoted to making it an efficient fighting weapon. It is the most crowded and highly organized of all fighting vessels.

THE HULL

STRUCTURALLY the submarine is like the fish—built to withstand water pressure from all sides and yet slip through the sea without resistance. It hangs suspended under the surface by making its weight equal to the weight of the water it displaces, and it can swim to right or left, up or down, and move forward with only the effort necessary to overcome friction. When it wishes to rise it ejects water ballast and acquires positive buoyancy, just as the old balloonist used to do by throwing sandbags out of his basket.

The principal factors which determine the hull *shape* are the pressure of the surrounding water and its fluid resistance. The submarine must withstand crushing forces of some seven tons per square foot at extreme depths, while still affording enough space within at ordinary pressure to accommodate the crew and much machinery. The vessel must also have inherent stability; that is, it must keep itself horizontal and right side up. Most submarines today are designed with an inner or "pressure" hull for stiffness, an outer ballast compartment of an oval shape, and a superstructure and conning tower. Earlier designs placed the ballast tanks within the pressure hull, but this has been given up because exterior tanks can more readily be shaped to stand hydrostatic pressure.

The pressure hull of the sub has a cylindrical cross section amidships, becoming elliptical fore and aft and tapering to a point at each end. It is built of steel plat-

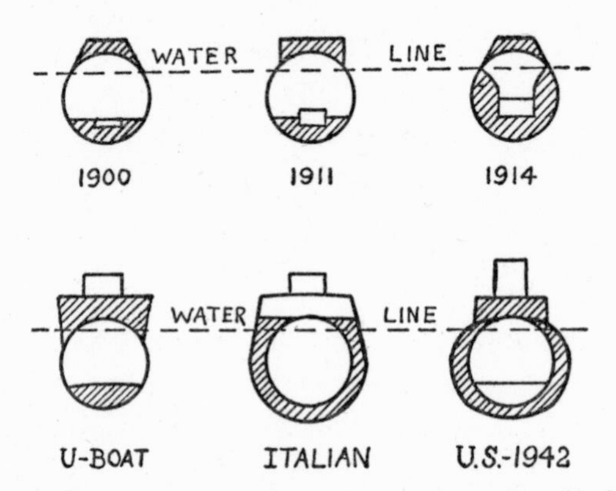

FIGURE 13. *Typical Shapes of Submarine Hulls*

ing supported on ring girders in the manner of underwater traffic tubes like the Holland Tunnel. Stiffness is improved by frequent disk-shaped bulkheads dividing the boat into several compartments, which may be isolated from one another by closing watertight doors. The submarine is also divided into a top and bottom half. A lengthwise deck separates the living space in the upper half from the bilges, which hold the various tanks, batteries, and heavy machinery.

The superstructure is a flat-topped platform whose

sides blend downward into the lines of the outer hull. It runs the length of the ship, being surmounted amidships by the conning tower. The purpose of the superstructure is to provide a flat deck for surface handling and gunnery, and to give the boat the usual seaworthy bow shape of the surface craft. The conning tower gives the equivalent of a ship's navigating bridge. All

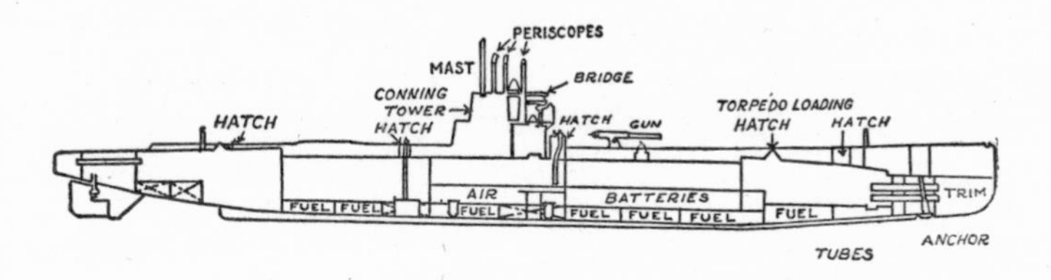

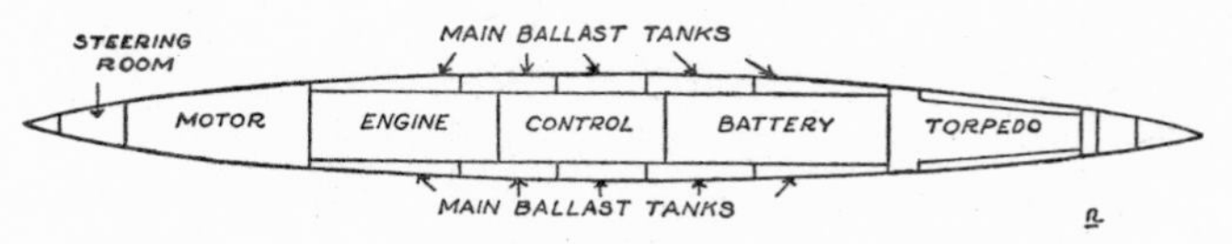

FIGURE 14. *Layout of an American Submarine*

spaces between superstructure and pressure hull are carefully vented so that air and water can flow in and out freely on submerging and surfacing.

Viewed from the side in cross section the submarine presents a series of compartments strung along the center line and separated by bulkheads. The number of these depends upon the size of the vessel. The accompanying drawing shows the layout of the *S-51*. Though she is an older boat her arrangement is typical of all subs. From bow to stern the compartments are: the torpedo room, battery room and living quarters; control room, engine room, motor room, and steering room. The small compartments at the extreme bow and stern are used for stowing anchor gear and for housing the trim tanks. This general arrangement is followed in all subs, though in later types there are two torpedo and battery rooms.

The submarine is entered through hatches in the conning tower and deck, giving access to at least three compartments. Special diagonal hatches are provided for loading ammunition and torpedoes. All entrance hatches open into cylindrical wells or trunks provided with ladders and closed by doors at the bottom. These trunks are for use in making underwater escapes, as will be described later.

The simplest way to become familiar with the intricacies of a sub's interior is to visit one compartment after another, examining the machinery spaces first, then ordnance compartments, and finally the control room.

THE ENGINE ROOM

SITUATED in the after part of the ship the engine room is the most crowded compartment on board. The main driving units are diesels burning heavy oil. All modern subs carry at least two engines, each turning its own propeller. In a few giants, such as the *Narwhal* and the *Nautilus,* there are four, two in line on each shaft. Each unit develops 1,535 horsepower, making a total of 6,140 for the boat. But these are exceptional.

Most subs operate on from 1,000 to 3,000 horsepower.

The diesel engine, as is well known, draws pure air into its cylinders at every power stroke and compresses it till its temperature rises to about 1,000° F. At the top of the stroke, fuel is injected by a pump, and burns rapidly, producing the power thrust on the piston. The advantages of the diesel for submarine propulsion are high economy, long life, and the absence of fire danger.

Engines of large horsepower draw in enormous quantities of air which must be continuously available at the intake ports of the cylinders. The air is brought to the engine room (or in small subs to the control room) by large ducts called "air-induction lines." These lead to openings high up on the conning tower, well protected from flying spray. They are fitted with machine-operated valves which must be solidly closed before submerging. Failure of these valves to close has been responsible for several disasters, among them the loss of the *Squalus*.

While the diesels are driving the boat on the surface the air inductions are locked open, as are also the bulkhead doors to the engine room. If this compartment should lose free access to outdoor air a high vacuum would be created so rapidly that the crew might die of burst lungs before rescue was possible. In the larger subs, such as the *Sailfish,* the air-induction openings on the conning tower are nearly three feet in diameter. The safety of the entire submarine depends upon their correct condition at all times.

The engine exhaust manifolds are taken off from

the outboard sides of the machines and passed through valves and through the pressure hull. These valves also are of prime importance, and must be closed tightly before a dive.

The engine room offers little space for anything but the main driving units, though there are various pumps for fuel, etc., located there. At the after end of each engine is a clutch for disconnecting it while running submerged on the electric motors.

THE MOTOR ROOM

THIS compartment is directly astern of the engine room and contains large direct-current electric motors on the same shafts as the diesels. These motors drive the boat while submerged. On the surface they operate as generators, receiving power from the engines and converting it to electricity for charging the storage batteries. A switchboard in the motor room is provided for changing connections. When working as generators the machines may be disconnected from the propeller shafts by clutches at the after end of the compartment.

Battery charging must be done on the surface. In wartime this is hazardous and is usually accomplished at night as rapidly as possible. Quick charging is effected by connecting the generators in parallel to give heavy currents. A series connection gives high power at low speeds when the machines are used as motors below. The batteries may also be charged slowly by "floating" the machines on the propeller shafts while the engines are driving the boat. In this case they absorb only a fraction of the power and merely keep the batteries filled in the manner of an automobile installation. Still another connection eliminates the motors altogether, and their rotating parts simply ride along without using any power at all.

Diesel-electric drive, such as is used on railroad streamliners, is coming into favor for submarines also. In this arrangement the diesels drive electric generators entirely separate from the motors. On the surface, the current is fed to the motors, which drive the propellers, or it is used to charge the batteries. Below, the motors run on battery current as in other boats. The advantages are in the use of more compact and more powerful high-speed diesels, and in greater flexibility of control for wartime maneuvering.

The motor room contains various auxiliary machinery, such as the air compressors, pumps, hydraulic gear, and many other minor devices. There is often a miniature machine shop crowded into this compartment for making repairs away from port. Special motor-generator sets for supplying the gyrocompass and listening equipment are also installed here. The motor room is the electrical headquarters of the ship.

THE BATTERY ROOM

THIS compartment is placed just forward of the control room (and just aft of it also, if there are two). The batteries are of the lead-sulphuric-acid type and are set as low as possible into the bottom of the boat because of their great weight. They are several feet high, totally enclosed in rubber cells, and are capable of storing many thousand ampere-hours of energy. They will usually drive the ship twenty-four hours or more at a speed of two or three knots after a full charge. If the submarine must escape from its enemies underwater, the batteries can drive it as fast as ten knots. But the energy will be used up in about an hour. The problem of getting clear away without exhausting the battery and becoming helpless is one of the most difficult that confronts a sub commander.

Batteries are usually divided into two banks of about 110 cells to furnish 120 or 240 volts. Heavy copper bars lead from them to the switchboard in the motor room aft. Small wires are also taken from the terminals of each cell to a test board above so that the state of charge may be constantly checked. Certain "pilot" cells are accessible through hatches in the deck for making specific-gravity readings with a hydrometer. In the larger subs the battery wells are big enough for an electrician to climb down into for inspections.

The current is used to operate many auxiliaries, such as periscope-raising gear, anchor-winch motors, and steering engines. The later vessels have many electrically operated valves and controls also. All submarines use current for lighting, cooking, refrigeration, radio and communication circuits.

The lead-acid battery gives off hydrogen both on charge and discharge and generates deadly chlorine gas when flooded with salt water. Hence good ventilation is essential. Special ducts are provided, with blowers, to exhaust gases overboard on the surface and into the battery rooms when submerged. A hydrogen detector is in operation continuously when underway. Concentrations of more than 3 per cent cause an alarm to ring before there is an explosive mixture of oxygen and hydrogen present. Chlorine is never given off unless the battery is accidentally flooded with salt water. The only control for it is to seal the compartment at once.

THE TORPEDO ROOM

THIS compartment is the sub's principal reason for being and is comparable to the turrets on a battleship. The torpedo tubes are installed in two tiers side by side at the forward end. There may be four or six forward and two or four aft (when there is an after torpedo room). The tubes are about twenty-five feet long and project some distance into the room. They are bronze cylinders, closed at the rear end by tight-fitting hinged doors, and at the front end by watertight muzzle doors. They extend beyond this and terminate at the outer part of the pressure hull, where movable caps are fitted which blend with the shape of the vessel.

The tube is loaded by closing the outboard doors and draining the water, then opening the inner door. The torpedo fits snugly in the bore and cannot be fired till the loading door is closed and dogged down and both outer doors are opened. The three are interlocked mechanically. Firing is done by blowing a shot of compressed air in behind the torpedo. The operation can be accomplished by a man standing beside the tube, or from the control room by electrical means. When the submarine is in a tight spot the commander usually fires the tubes himself while following his intended victim in the periscope.

The torpedo room is somewhat less crowded than other compartments, space being required for reloading the tubes. Two to six extra torpedoes are carried in racks on the walls. They are picked up by a chain hoist and rope sling suspended from an I-beam running along the roof, and are balanced by the crew as they are pushed forward into the tubes.

Details of the firing devices are kept secret, but the general principle is that the torpedo is set in motion internally on firing by tripping levers set in the tube. Aiming may be done by a torpedoman by hand, or it may be made continuous and automatic by remote control. Firing mechanisms are so arranged that the whole group of tubes can be set off at once if desired.

THE TANKS

THOUGH not actually compartments the various tanks aboard a submarine are large enough and important enough to be included in this category. Most vital of them are the ballast tanks which control the total weight of the boat and cause it to sink or rise. The general scheme is to provide large spaces, either inside or outside the pressure hull, which may be flooded with sea water or pumped out at will. With these tanks empty the submarine has "positive buoyancy," which it loses when they are full.

The ballast tanks are divided into main tanks, regulator tanks, and bow and stern trimming tanks. When the boat is on the surface and is about to dive, the main tanks are filled. Then enough water is put into the regulator to give only a very slight positive buoyancy—a few hundred pounds. The sub will then slide under with the help of her horizontal planes. Once below, the trimming tanks are watered to give her exact fore-and-aft balance.

The reserve buoyancy runs from 20 to 33 per cent of the total submerged displacement. Most of it is destroyed by filling the main ballasts, which are very large and are placed around the girth of the vessel amidships. These tanks are subdivided by bulkheads which prevent the water from surging back and forth and upsetting the balance of the boat. As diving is a high-speed operation, the tanks must be flooded very quickly. This is done by opening large "kingston valves" in their bottoms and at the same time opening vents on top. Each tank has several kingstons, and the whole volume can be flooded in about sixty seconds. Even the giant *Surcouf,* largest submarine ever built, could submerge totally in two minutes. For "crash dives," when overtaken by the enemy, every tank is flooded simultaneously. The Germans are said to hasten the process by connecting the tank vents to the suction end of the air compressors, thus flooding the ship even more quickly.

In the normal submerged run the kingstons are left open, the tanks being brim full. When it is desired to come up the tanks are "blown" with high-pressure air carried in large quantities for the purpose. This only removes part of the water; the rest is pumped out, after buoyancy is restored, and discharged into a main drain running along the keel. Compressed air is furnished by large compressors in the engine or motor room and is stored in groups of steel bottles placed in the bilges, usually under the control room. It is carried at about 3,000 pounds per square inch and fed through a distributing manifold to the various tanks. A reducing valve brings the working pressure down to 200 pounds.

Fuel and lubricating oil tanks are situated close to the engines. Since the ship must retain her exact weight at all times for proper operation, sea water is admitted to these tanks in the exact amount necessary to compensate for the weight of oil lost in running. The water does not mix with the oil.

The successful operation of the submarine depends on the careful adjustment of these masses of water and fuel, which is an expert job. The weight of the local sea water must be accurately known, for instance, for it changes with sea temperature and from ocean to ocean. The fresh water in rivers and harbors is about 3 per cent lighter, so that in going from port into the open ocean changes in ballast must be made. The submarine must even be compensated for the loss of weight occasioned by firing torpedoes, or by the absence of members of the crew. One sub found readjustments necessary after having been given a new coat of paint in drydock.

AUXILIARY COMPARTMENTS

THERE is a large number of pumps, compressors, and valve-operating machinery to be located about the interior of a submarine. In large boats the ballast and bilge pumps are gathered in one room in the bilges and are presided over by a man who understands their use intimately. In the smaller boats this equipment is located in the engine and motor rooms.

At the extreme bow a small compartment provides storage for the mushroom anchor and chain and contains the machinery to raise and lower it. A folding anchor is carried in a recess in the ship's side, and its chain, too, is stowed in this room. The anchor winches are operated either by compressed air or by electric motors.

Way aft is the steering compartment, containing the electric-motor-driven steering engine.

The design of submarines varies somewhat with size and class, and there may be many more compartments than those enumerated. The machinery, however, is essentially the same in all.

THE CONTROL ROOM AND CONNING TOWER

THIS is the nerve center of the submarine—the room which contains the hundreds of gauges, control wheels, levers, indicating instruments, and electric circuits for co-ordinating the action of the boat. It is difficult to give a complete description; only the more general features will be touched upon.

In the center of the compartment the two (sometimes three) periscopes protrude downward from overhead. They are steel cylinders about a foot in diameter, with handles and an eyepiece at their lower ends. When fully lowered they drop into wells in the deck. Erected for use they come to comfortable height of a man standing.

The periscope is essentially a telescope with a barrel which can be elongated to protrude as much as thirty feet above the control room. In its upper end is a watertight glass window, a prism to bend the light from the horizontal downward, and a system of lenses for focusing and erecting the image. A mirror and several combinations of lenses at the bottom turn the light toward the observer and provide him with different magnifications. One handle controls this change while the other tilts the upper prism and gives the instrument up-and-down sweep. The whole mechanism turns freely through 360 degrees. A glass plate in the focal plane is graduated in degrees and is provided with cross hairs, and thus works as a range finder.

If the operator can estimate the height of the object he is looking at through his periscope he can compute from the scale how far away it is.

The forward bulkhead of the control room mounts the steering wheel and forward and after plane-control wheels, and beside them a repeating dial for the gyro-compass. A chart table and other navigating aids are near by. The space is also filled with many dials, reading depth under water, trim of the boat, etc. At one side are more dials and scales reading the angle of dive, barometric pressure, propeller r.p.m., air-manifold pressure, tank conditions, and in fact every item of data for the whole boat. Along both sides are ranged the levers and valve wheels which operate the kingstons, air vents, pumps, and other equipment for controlling buoyancy and trim. Prominent on one wall is the inclinometer, a kind of spirit level which shows the angle of dive. To avoid spilling the acid out of the batteries this angle is never allowed to go beyond 15 degrees.

One of the most important devices present is the electric indicator board, covered with red and green lights—affectionately known as the "Christmas Tree"—which shows the condition of every hull opening and valve which affects the tightness of the boat, together with all mechanical matters essential to diving. The red lights are on when main induction lines, exhaust valves, conning tower, etc., are open. The greens do not replace them till all are closed and locked. A "green board" is the requisite condition before starting a dive.

One corner of the control room is given over to the radio "shack." Modern radio equipment permits communicating through the water for several miles, either with other subs, with surface vessels, or sometimes with airplanes. When the submarine is up, her radio range is equal to that of any other ship.

Telephone equipment of the selector type is also provided, so that the control room can talk to any other compartment by dialing it. Much of the operation in the engine room and motor room is carried on with the aid of headphones, as the machinery makes too much noise for conversation.

Directly above the center of the control room, outside the pressure hull, is the conning tower. This is a steel chamber of elliptical shape containing further instruments and providing access through hatchways to the navigating bridge above. The latter is a narrow space surrounded by high bulwarks and occupied by a magnetic compass, gyrorepeater, steering wheel and communicating systems. In passing it should be noted that gyrorepeaters are dials which duplicate the reading on the main gyrocompass which is installed in one of the compartments below. The repeaters all follow the master exactly, being controlled by electric circuits.

Everything on the bridge is watertight and can be "secured" for diving in a few seconds. Submergence requires that the hatches to the conning tower be closed and dogged down. On the rear part of the bridge is a retractable mast, normally erected on the surface. This is used for raising signal hoists when operating with other naval vessels, and for carrying running lights at night in peacetime. The radio antenna consists of two wires running fore and aft on masts of their own which flank the bridge. Faired into the bridge structure are the stuffing glands for the periscopes, which slide up and down in watertight seals.

EXTERNAL HULL EQUIPMENT

THE minimum of obstructions is allowed on the outside of the submarine, since streamlining is of great importance to economical operation submerged. The deck, fore and aft of the conning tower, is narrow and is composed of wooden gratings buttoned securely in place. Most of our subs have only one gun, installed either forward or aft of the conning tower, and one or more machine guns on the bridge. The gun mechanisms are waterproof. Muzzle plugs and canvas breech covers are put in place before a dive.

Anchor and docking gear are contained within the hull. At bow and stern horizontal steering planes are recessed into the sides of the ship on swivel joints. When submerged these are swung out at right angles, and in this position they turn like rudders to send the ship up or down. A sub is ordinarily brought to the surface without blowing her tanks, by setting these planes at the proper angle.

The only other obstruction is a light guard rail which surrounds the deck space and is permanently fixed. It offers very little resistance, and is necessary to protect the crew in rough weather.

LIVING ACCOMMODATIONS

SPACE is at such a premium in submarines that the men must live literally in the midst of the machinery. Battery and torpedo rooms, being least crowded, are fitted with most of the crew's bunks and lockers. The bunks are arranged in double tiers along the center line, four berths high; the lockers are built in along the sides wherever there is room.

The "officers' country" is usually well forward. In small subs it amounts to no more than a few berths, a washstand, and desk, the top of the latter being used for a mess table. In the larger boats the commanding officer has a cabin of his own, and a space is set aside as a wardroom.

The galley is usually located in the after battery room (if any), electric range and refrigerator at one side and storage lockers in the middle, on the smooth top of which the men eat standing up. Toilet arrangements are complicated by the fact that waste must be forced overboard by air pressure, and the operation involves considerable machinery. The toilet is a standard means of signaling to the surface when the sub is disabled on the bottom. A bucket of oil is thrown into it and blown clear, rising at once to make a telltale slick on the sea.

The sub's interior is brilliantly lighted, and the air is kept in circulation by a blower system. The new boats are being equipped with air-conditioning units on account of the preponderance of tropical service in this war. Each compartment is stocked with emergency rations, life preservers, and enough Momsen escape lungs to supply the entire crew. In addition, there are oxygen bottles and cans of carbon-dioxide absorbent ready to hand. A CO_2 detector is available for use on long dives, when the air is rebreathed so much as to become vitiated.

Every possible measure of comfort is provided within the space allowed, and the crews are invariably satisfied. The skill of their work and the adventurous character of the service make up for the soda fountains, boxing bouts, and movies of the larger vessels. The man counts himself proud who has the qualifications to be allowed to live aboard a submarine.

THE TORPEDO

ENEMY torpedoes seldom fall into the hands of their intended victims. If the missile does not explode it sinks automatically at the end of its run and is lost. Neither side can afford to have a live explosive loose on the sea. Thus the exact design of competing makes is not well known. However, the principles of all are the same.

Present British and American practice standardizes on a torpedo twenty-one inches in diameter and from twenty to twenty-four feet long. An eighteen-inch size is used on some high-speed motorboats and torpedo planes. Like the submarine the torpedo is divided into compartments. At the forward end is the war head of TNT. Next come the air flask, the compensating chamber, and the engine room. At the stern is the gyroscope and the steering compartment.

Since the sole object of the torpedo is to hit a small target at a great distance, it must move as rapidly as possible to make aiming calculations simpler, and to afford the enemy less time to turn out of its path. This means enormous power in a small space. Compressed air at nearly 3,000 pounds per square inch is used because it gives the highest concentration of energy.

The air is stored in a steel flask occupying about half the length of the torpedo. It is fed aft to the engines through a reducing valve and mixer which injects water and alcohol, a combination known as "pink lady" to the sailors. This is ignited and burns furiously, supplying a blast of superheated steam, air, and gas for propulsion. The American torpedo uses two small turbines driven in opposite directions by the combustion gases issuing from nozzles. The exhaust is piped overboard.

The turbines are installed one behind the other and are connected to two concentric shafts, which in turn drive two propellers. The opposite rotation is necessary to prevent the torpedo itself from revolving by reaction. Details of the power plant are kept secret. They represent seventy years of intensive development which has crammed 400 horsepower into the space of a small nail keg. Since air expanding from high pressure becomes very cold, an alcohol flame is placed inside the air flask to preheat it. A second burner acts only on starting to ignite the combustible mixture. Both flames are kindled by powder cartridges set off by a trigger at the time of firing.

The torpedo's system of control is even more beautifully worked out than its propulsion. The heart of it is a tiny gyroscope placed near the stern and set spinning at 18,000 r.p.m. by air jets. The gyro's flywheel is about the diameter of an ash tray and weighs only two pounds. Yet at this enormous speed it rules the

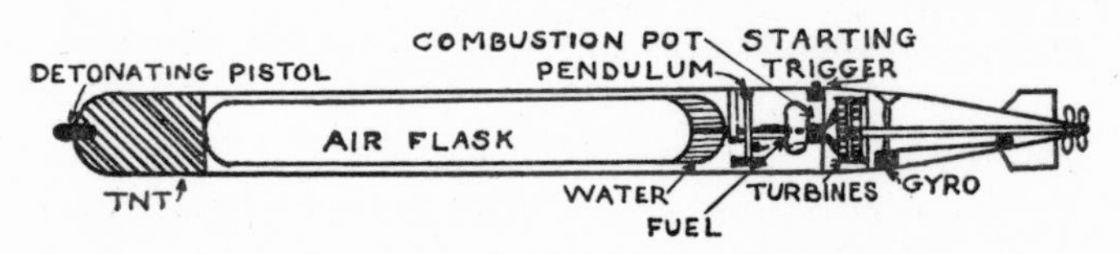

FIGURE 15. *Interior of a Torpedo*

missile's course with irresistible force. The framework which carries the spinning wheel is mounted in ball bearings and is free to turn. It is connected through linkages to a small air motor which works the vertical rudder astern. Upon firing, it is not the torpedo but the gyro which is carefully aimed at the target. Once in the water this automatic steersman immediately pulls the missile into the correct course and holds it there. Contrary to common belief the submarine does not have to be pointed at its victim to fire accurately. Torpedoes can be launched in any direction within sixty degrees or so of the right course.

To keep the little "tin fish" at a constant depth the compensating chamber is left open to the sea. Water pressure actuates a steel and rubber diaphragm against the pressure of a spring. The motion is transmitted through an air motor to horizontal rudders at the stern. Before launching, the spring tension is set to correspond with any desired depth. As soon as the run has begun, the missile will sink until spring and water pressure balance, and it will travel thereafter at that level. The slight lag in this mechanism formerly caused the torpedo to plunge or "porpoise," sometimes breaking surface and leaping into the air. This trouble has been cured by a sensitive pendulum which operates on the steering vanes to keep a steady horizontal course.

Loss of air and fuel during the run lightens the torpedo by several hundred pounds. This is neutralized by an equal weight of water admitted to the compensating chamber by a special mechanism.

The modern war head is packed with 600 pounds of TNT to be touched off by a "pistol" in the nose. The latter is a steel pin which is driven back on contact to strike a percussion cap. While in the submarine the pistol is locked and a safety device does not release it till the torpedo's propeller shaft has turned a set number of revolutions. The Navy keeps the method of aiming and launching the missile a close secret. In principle it is done by remote control, the position of the gyroscope being under direct manipulation of the firing officer continuously during the period of approach and aim. All the inner works of the torpedo are started by triggers which are tripped as the torpedo is blown out of its tube. The only unsolved problem is the "impulse bubble" of air which breaks the surface with a very noticeable splash directly over the submarine immediately after firing. This gives the sub's position away to observers above, and frequently draws down a devastating depth charge attack.

Torpedoes weigh from 1,500 to 1,800 pounds and can travel nearly fifty knots. The long-range type has a striking distance of better than 10,000 yards. These missiles are made by the government only, employing workmen of the highest skill and precision. They cost more than $10,000 apiece, and are consequently never wasted. In torpedo practice the TNT in the head is replaced with water. An ingenious device blows the water out at the end of the target run so that the missile rises and floats, to be picked up by a salvage crew.

The greatest permissible error at a range of 4,000 yards is fifty-five yards to right or left and not more than two feet vertically. The torpedo is usually set for a depth of fifteen to twenty feet against a battleship and from four to ten feet against destroyers and merchantmen. Its mechanism is so extremely accurate that misses are almost invariably the result of poor aim or faulty calculation of the enemy's speed or distance. To date no efficient means has been found to nullify a torpedo explosion. The nearest thing to it is the double-bottom compartmentation of the warship. Merchantmen cannot afford space for this, and are always seriously damaged when hit. The world is still waiting for a device that will nullify the torpedo.

TYPES AND DUTIES OF AMERICAN SUBMARINES

ALL OUR recently built submarines are designed with sufficient range and surface speed to enable them to operate with the fleet. They are organized into groups similar to other fighting vessels. The basic unit is the division, comprised of six boats under a division commander, who is also the captain of one of them. Two or more divisions make up a squadron, which likewise has its commanding officer. One or several squadrons may be assigned to duty with each major naval force, or any number of them may operate independently. When operating with fleet units all squadron commanders receive their orders direct from the officer in charge of the force.

The submarine branch, though described as a "service," is not separate and distinct as is the naval air force. Like the destroyer, cruiser, or battleship the sub is simply a specialized type of vessel to be assigned to any duty the naval command may deem necessary. There is no senior officer in charge of all undersea vessels. Like all other types of ship the submarine receives specialized attention from a group of officers and personnel in the Navy Department in Washington.

In port each submarine squadron is based on a mother ship, such as the *Holland* or the *Canopus*. These are large naval auxiliaries fitted with complete repair and refueling facilities, spare torpedoes, and ship's stores. Mother ships do not accompany fleet units to battle but remain in port for servicing the subs as they come in.

In conjunction with battle forces of various kinds the submarines perform scout and attack duties suitable to their character. When proceeding in formation in the open sea they are found in front and on the outskirts of the group, searching for the enemy and keeping a lookout for mines. When the battle is joined they deploy according to the needs of the situation and attack the enemy's units with torpedoes. Their duties depend entirely on the size and make-up of the opponent. In modern naval warfare the tendency is to break up large fighting units into smaller task forces, which may have no submarines at all, or which may send numbers of them ahead to reconnoiter their objective.

Following the German practice the American submarine has become increasingly a self-sufficient weapon striking on its own. On this service it may go out in squadrons, in divisions, several together, or singly. Its value in reconnaissance is extremely high, for it can penetrate the enemy's position and watch his movements without being discovered, and then retire to communicate its findings to headquarters by radio. Individual submarines are often dispatched on special missions to harass the movement of enemy troops, and they may also be sent on long cruises to carry on commerce raiding wherever they may find victims in profitable quantity.

SUBMARINE WARFARE

REPRESENTATIVE U.S. SUBMARINES*

Names	*Displacement Surfc/Submgd*	*Length*	*Tubes*	*Guns*	*Crew*	*Other Data*
O–2 to 4, O–6 to 10	500/–	172½	4	1–3″	33	
R–1 to 7, R–9 to 20	530/680	186	4	1–3″		
S–11 to 13, S–14 to 17	790/	231	5	1–4″	38	
S 1, S–18 to 41	800/	219	4	1–4″		
S–48	1000/1458	267	4	1–4″	38	
S–42 to 47	850/1126	225	4	1–4″	38	
BARRACUDA, Bass, Bonita	2000/2506	341	6	1–3″ 2–M.G.	75	12,000 mi. radius
ARGONAUT	2710/4080	381	4	2–6″	89	mine layer 60 mines
NARWHAL, Nautilus	2730/3960	371	6	2–6″	88	19 knot surface
DOLPHIN	1540/2215	319	6	1–4″	63	17 knot surface
CACHALOT, Cuttlefish	1110/1650	271	6	1–3″	45	
PIKE, Porpoise, Shark, Tarpon	1310/1934	301	6	1–3″ 1–M.G.	50	12,000 mi. radius
PERCH, Pickerel, Permit, Plunger, Pollock, Pompano	1330/1998	300½	6	1–3″ 1–M.G.	50	
SALMON, Seal, Skipjack, Snapper, Sturgeon, Stingray	1450/2198	298	8	1–3″ 1–M.G.	55	
SARGO, Saury, Seadragon, Sealion, Spearfish, Sculpin, Searaven, Seawolf, Sailfish, Swordfish	1450/–	310	8	1–3″ 1–M.G.	55	20 knots
MACKEREL, Marlin	800/–	253	6	1–3″ 2–M.G.	40	
THRESHER, Tambor, Tautog, Triton, Tuna, Trout	1450/–	299	8	1–3″ 2–M.G.	55	22 knots on trials
GRAMPUS, Gar, Grayling, Grayback, Grenadier, Gudgeon	1475/–	299	10	1–3″ 2–M.G.	—	
GATO, Greenling, Grouper, Growler, Grunion, Guardfish	1500/–	307	10	1–3″ 2–M.G.	—	21 knots
ALBACORE, Amberjack, Barb, Blackfish, Bluefish, Bonefish, Cod, Cero, Cowina, Darter, Drum, Flying Fish, Finback, Haddock, Halibut, Herring, Kingfish, Shad, Silversides, Trigger, Wahoo, Whale	1525/–	—	—	—	—	planned and building 1940–41 cruiser type
ANGLER, Bashaw, Bluegill, Bream, Cavalla, Cobia, Croaker, Dace, Dorado, Flasher, Flier, Flounder, Gabilan, Gunnel, Gurnard, Haddo, Hake, Harder, Hoe, Jack, Lapon, Mingo, Muskallonge, Paddie, Pargo, Peto, Pogy, Pompon, Puffer, Rasher, Raton, Ray, Redfin, Robalo, Rock, Runner, Sawfish, Scamp, Scorpion, Snook, Steelhead, Sunfish, Tunny	1525/–	—	—	—	—	No further information available

* From *The Ships and Aircraft of the United States Fleet,* by James C. Fahey.

The accompanying table gives most of the types of United States subs now in commission, numbering between 20 and 180. Many more not mentioned are either just launched or have been laid down. An additional hundred submarines have lately been authorized, and there is talk of increasing the fleet still further—a strong tribute to the deadliness of undersea warfare.

With the exception of the *Mackerel* and the *Marlin,* which are 800-ton coastal boats, all our newer subs are of approximately 1,450 tons surface displacement, with surface speeds close to twenty knots and a cruising range better than 12,000 miles. We have only three very large craft, the *Narwhal,* the *Nautilus,* and the *Argonaut.* This supertype has not been duplicated, presumably because it is not as maneuverable as the smaller sub. The *Argonaut* is the only boat listed as a mine layer; she carries sixty mines. The *S-1* alone is credited with carrying a plane.

The larger subs require as many as five officers, the smallest only three. Most of the boats carry from fifteen to twenty torpedoes. The cost of the average submarine is about $5,000,000.

CHAPTER FIVE

THE SUBMARINE'S CREW AND HOW IT FUNCTIONS

SUBMARINE duty is by far the most technical of any in the service, and all hands must be mechanical experts. Exact timing and perfect execution are required in every detail of operation. A single mistake may cost the Navy a ship, and the men their lives. The space is so confined that every officer and man has many duties. There can be neither laxity of discipline nor failure of hand or brain.

Crew and officers operate as a professional team, every member knowing the theory and practice of the whole ship. Though each department is manned by specialists, their work can be done by most of the others in case of need. Emergencies may segregate men in an unaccustomed compartment; they must know every valve and lever in it as intimately as if it were their habitual charge.

The organization of the sub's crew is the same as with any ship, with officers of varying rank at the top, chief petty officers in charge of departments, and petty officers and sailors of various ratings making up the remainder. But space is so limited that a unique spirit of comradeship is necessary. Although the men address their officers as "Captain," "Lieutenant," etc., the officers call the men by their first names and often by nicknames. The atmosphere is one of mutual respect and confidence, and there is a kindly consideration on all sides. There is no prouder or more unified group of naval men than those who man our subs.

THE OFFICERS AND THEIR DUTIES

THE commanding officer, or captain, as he is usually called, has the rank of lieutenant (senior grade), or lieutenant commander if the sub is large. His duty is to take the full responsibility for the ship when he is aboard and to make all important decisions. It is the captain who, when receiving word of an enemy approaching, plans the attack, maneuvers the boat into position, follows the target in the periscope, and gives the order to fire the torpedoes. It is also his duty to watch every member of the crew closely to see that no one is failing in morale or efficiency, and to make sure that all are as comfortable and content as possible. In case of disaster it is the captain who must make the split-second decisions that mean coming out alive. No matter what his subordinates may think, they are ready to obey instantly, even to sacrificing their lives for the welfare of the others.

Under the captain's supervision the many operational duties on board are divided among the other officers, each taking several. These duties are those of the executive and navigation officers; the torpedo, engineering, electrical, diving, communications, and commissary officers.

The "exec" is second in command and acts as general manager for the whole organization.

The *navigation officer* "cons" the ship, i.e., lays the courses and is responsible for arriving at such destination as the captain may order. The actual work of steering is done by a quartermaster under his orders.

The *torpedo officer* has charge of all ordnance on board and must maintain the torpedoes and tubes and all firing circuits and other gear in perfect shape at all times. He also has charge of the deck gun and machine guns, ammunition magazines and the work of replenishing gunnery stores.

The *engineering officer* has charge of all engine-room apparatus as well as the various mechanical systems such as pumps, air compressors, hydraulic lines, the working of valves and control mechanisms.

The main duties of the *electrical officer* are the care of the batteries and motors and all electric circuits on the boat, as well as the maintenance of the gyrocompass.

It is the duty of the *diving officer* to take charge during the special operation of submerging—the most critical moment in the running of the sub. He sees that all men are at their posts, all hull openings closed, all tanks and valves in the proper condition for an undersea run, then carries out the actual process of taking on ballast, diving the ship, and steadying her on an even keel below. Conversely, he brings the ship up when the captain is ready to surface. It is this officer's specialty to know accurately the capacities and buoyancy effects of all tanks and to understand how to trim the ship under every condition. He shares with the engineering officer knowledge of the fuel supply, and with the torpedo officer information on the amount of ordnance on board. His many duties make him one of the most important men on the ship; it is he who must have a sixth sense to guide him by "feel" when the vessel is navigating blind below.

The *communications officer* is responsible for the telephone and other signal circuits in the boat as well as for the radio and listening systems. One of his duties is to take charge of and keep up to date the secret code by which one Navy ship communicates with another. In event of capture it is his job to destroy the code book before it falls into enemy hands. His work is among the most secret on the ship, for the latest sound locators and radio apparatus are items the enemy would give much to possess.

The *commissary officer* is the housekeeper of the boat, seeing to ship's stores and planning the buying and stocking of food. He is also charged with the general welfare and comfort of the crew.

On the average submarine all these duties are divided among four or five men who must have specialized knowledge in many fields. Any one of the officers is capable of taking any other's job in an emergency. One reason why young officers are so eager to get submarine duty is that a few years of it give them a more thorough all-round training in naval technique than a lifetime on other types of ship. This duty also offers a unique opportunity for initiative and the development of self-reliance and good judgment.

THE CREW AND ITS DUTIES

THE number of enlisted men in a sub's crew varies from thirty on the O-type training boats to eighty-four on the *Argonaut*. They are divided roughly into the same departments as their officers, though each sailor is confined to a relatively few duties in normal times. All the enlisted men aboard are petty officers or chief petty officers, i. e., rated men with specialties, as differentiated from the ordinary seamen found on battleships. The submarine carries several chiefs who are old-timers with from ten to twenty years' experience in the "pig boats," men who are past masters at their several arts.

The senior C.P.O. is called "Chief-of-the-Boat." He and the other chiefs usually assume certain of the duties above enumerated for the officers. Thus a *chief torpedoman* may be in command of the torpedo room, or a *chief electrician's mate* be responsible for the electrical department. A *chief machinist's mate* is usually found aboard, though not commonly in full charge of the machinery. These men are as a rule older and often with more years of service than the officers themselves, and fit into the organization as practical technicians. Like everyone else on board they have a tremendous pride of accomplishment and insist on remaining in the submarine branch. Even so, most of them are under thirty-five. The undersea service is a young man's game.

The crew ratings commonly found on submarines are:

Torpedomen	Quartermasters
Machinist's Mates	Signalmen
Electrician's Mates	Pharmacist's Mates
Gunner's Mates	Yeomen
Firemen	Cooks
Radiomen	Messboys
Fire Controlmen	An occasional specialist

These ratings are self-explanatory. Most of the crew are found among the ratings in the first column. There is usually one pharmacist's mate, who does duty as a doctor (all officers aboard have had first-aid training), one yeoman, who keeps the ship's records and operating log, one cook, who has to be good, and two or three messboys. Fire controlmen are specialists handling the aiming and firing of the guns and torpedo tubes. But it must be remembered that every man may have to assume other duties and so must have a working knowledge of all his buddies' jobs.

THE SUBMARINE ON THE SURFACE

AT THE dock, getting underway, and running on the surface the submarine is managed precisely like any ordinary ship. Handling the boat in close quarters or at docks is done by the captain and other officers from

Machinist's Mate

Electrician's Mate

Cook

Signalman

Radioman

Gunner's Mate

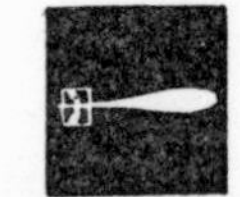
Torpedoman

Fire Controlman

Quartermaster

Pharmacist's Mate

Yeoman

FIGURE 16. *Insignia of the Ratings in the Submarine Service*

the bridge. Only the few crew members with work to do remain on deck. A signalman and a quartermaster have bridge duties; one or two others may be employed as messengers.

On the surface the ship has several feet of freeboard, and in good weather her decks will be dry and her hatches open. All possible fresh air is gotten below against the time when the dive shuts it off. Navigation may be done by magnetic compass or by the gyro-repeater. There is room on the bridge to lay out a chart, to take bearings, to shoot the sun, and to carry out all other ordinary duties in directing the boat. The radioman is on duty below to receive and transmit orders. During surface runs many of the crew are not on watch, and are allowed to lie in their bunks or sit about in the torpedo and battery rooms. But in wartime, when the sub is in the open sea, all hands are prepared for instant action in case of Battle Stations. A crash dive may be called for at any moment.

Rough weather covers a sub with white water and forces everything to be closed but the conning-tower hatch. Ventilation air is then obtained from the induction lines. All deck gear has been secured; guns covered, and wind screens set on the bridge. In this condition the submarine can ride out a storm as well as any surface craft, in fact better, being so nearly submerged. But surface running in a seaway is uncomfortable. The ship rolls and pitches heavily, and the men below must lie down or else hang onto something to keep out of the machinery. In the absence of a visual horizon a man's equilibrium is affected, and he must be a good sailor to take this kind of beating and enjoy it.

Much of a sub's time on the surface is occupied in charging her batteries, in lying to, or in making long transoceanic runs. The latter duty is arduous in wartime because of the constant threat of being sighted by the enemy. Yet submerged runs are only made when the risk is too great above. To realize the greatest economy the ship must plug along at about half speed twenty-four hours a day.

THE DIVE

The most important function, for which the crew is incessantly trained, is to slip quietly and quickly beneath the sea on a few sharp commands. Diving puts a supreme test on the crew, for it is in the transition from ship to fish that most accidents happen. A single error anywhere in the complicated team play can drop the boat like a stone to crushing depths. Diving may be carried only to "periscope depth" or it may send the boat down to her pressure limit, which is on the order of 300 feet. Periscope depth, with the eye a foot or two above water, puts the keel about thirty feet down.

The captain's order, "Rig ship for diving!" is passed through the boat by voice and telephone, so that all receive it in a few seconds. All hands spring immediately to their diving stations. Talk ceases entirely; smoking stops. Every officer and man has a definite sequence of duties readying his part of the ship, down to the cook, who must "secure" the kitchen sink. When all preliminaries are done the men stand ready at their posts. This first phase is largely a matter of testing all apparatus which will go into use in the dive. It includes securing all hatches, rigging out the diving planes, testing the operating gear for main inductions, kingstons, high-pressure air, etc. As each compartment is made ready the officer or man in charge reports by telephone to the diving officer in the control room: "Torpedo room rigged for diving," "Engine room rigged for diving," and so on. When all reports are in, the diving officer informs the captain that the ship is rigged for diving.

The captain now orders all men on the bridge below, then follows them down the conning-tower hatch, which is closed by one of the control-room watch. The skipper takes his station in the middle of the control room and gives the order: "Stand by for diving!" The diving officer sings out, "Sound the alarm!" and immediately klaxons in every compartment shriek out the warning. This is a ready signal, putting every man on his toes for co-ordinated action.

Orders now follow one another in quick succession: "Open main ballast kingstons!" "Open main ballast vents!" "Open vents on bow buoyancy!" "Stop main engines!" "Secure main exhaust lines!"—and many more. As each order is given it is picked up by the telephone orderly and relayed to the proper compartment. In a moment word comes back that it has been carried out, and the orderly repeats the fact back to the diving officer. At the same time a red light burning on the "Christmas Tree" is replaced by a green one. In a moment the only red lights remaining indicate that the main inductions are still open. The ship must breathe fresh air till the last.

One final order secures the main inductions. As a final test the diving officer orders a shot of air bled from the high-pressure manifold as he watches the barometer. If the needle moves up and remains steady, the boat is watertight. He then turns to the captain and reports: "Pressure in the boat; green board, sir." The last red light has flicked out on the "Christmas Tree."

The next order is: "Dive!" or "Take her down!" The klaxons blow a second time; men everywhere make the motions in unison that long training has taught them. Electric motors are started; their gentle whine replaces the earlier roar of the engines. All around is the thunder of water surging into tanks, the blubbering of air venting on deck. "Down bow planes, ten degrees!" A quartermaster spins a big wheel at one side and repeats: "Down bow planes, ten degrees!" The quiet confidence of the low voices is like the words of the surgeons around an operating table.

The submarine, losing buoyancy, slides down into the sea.

Watching his inclinometer and trim gauges keenly, the diving officer orders water into the regulator tank, into bow or stern trim, till he has his ship in perfect balance. In every compartment men are watching for the slightest sign that all is not right.

"Steady at fifty feet," murmurs the captain. The order is repeated. The large black hand on the depth gauge climbs to 50, then rests there as the quartermaster adjusts his planes. The ship is submerged. *This entire series of orders and acts can be accomplished in sixty seconds.*

If the run is to be made at periscope depth for surface observation, the order, "Up, periscope," is given.

One or more of the instruments is hoisted by its motor, and the captain fits his eye to the rubber cup, adjusts for magnification and angle with the handles, and surveys the world he has just left.

If the trip is totally submerged, periscopes are left housed; the ship is leveled at 100 feet, or some other

FIGURE 17. *Scene in the Control Room at Periscope Depth*

safe depth, and thereafter navigates blind on a course indicated by the gyrocompass. In the unlikely event that the gyro is disabled, steering can be done by reading the magnetic compass on the bridge through a system of lenses and mirrors. During the run below, a part of the crew is on watch while the rest stand by for action if an emergency should come.

Resurfacing the sub is done in the reverse manner, and even more quickly. Bow planes are elevated, and the ship simply climbs to the top; main ballasts are blown, and the boat emerges; main inductions are opened and main engines started; the conning tower is opened and the bridge manned. The captain and navigation officer return to the topside. The dive is finished.

There are three ways to submerge the ship: (1) the standing dive, in which the boat is stationary in the water and simply sinks by losing buoyancy; (2) the ordinary dive underway, above described; and (3) the crash dive, used when the submarine is running for cover when chased by an enemy. The latter, being most vital in battle, is practiced repeatedly. Ability to crash dive in a given number of seconds is a principal item in a sub's acceptance tests, and the faster it can be done the prouder is the crew. In actual battle, when the ship is under fire and perhaps already smashed about the superstructure, extraordinary speed must be used. It is then that the long training of the crew shows up, especially when damage may have put some of the important machinery out of service. It is then that the captain, knowing exactly how deep his boat can go from tables and tests, orders her down with confidence that she can get below the level of the depth charges that are sure to come.

BATTLE STATIONS

WHEN the submarine is cruising either above or at periscope depth and the enemy is sighted, the order to battle stations is given instantly and is backed up by a klaxon warning. If the fight is to be on the surface the gun crew piles on deck; the ammunition hatch is opened and a designated man, usually the cook, takes his station at the magazine to hand up shells. Meanwhile all others are at diving stations ready to execute a crash dive if necessary. The torpedo gang is standing by, too, with tubes loaded and at the ready. More than one U-boat has missed her target because her inexperienced torpedo crew failed to be prepared.

In danger zones the sub usually spends the daylight hours at periscope depth with an officer constantly on watch at the eyepiece. Word of the approach of the quarry brings all hands to battle stations on the instant. The captain mans the periscope and maneuvers the boat into a position that will be close to the course of the intended victim. As he does this he must estimate her speed and heading and calculate the angle of fire. Meanwhile the torpedo room is standing by with its missiles ready.

Making a hit on a moving vessel a mile or more away is like bagging a flying duck with a rifle: the torpedo must be fired at a point *ahead* of the target by exactly the right amount. This means that the course of the missile and the line of sight at the moment of firing make a certain angle. When all the data are collected this angle is computed by the captain's assistants and is translated into a torpedo heading, which is either telephoned to the torpedo room for manual setting, or is set automatically by a fire-control mechanism

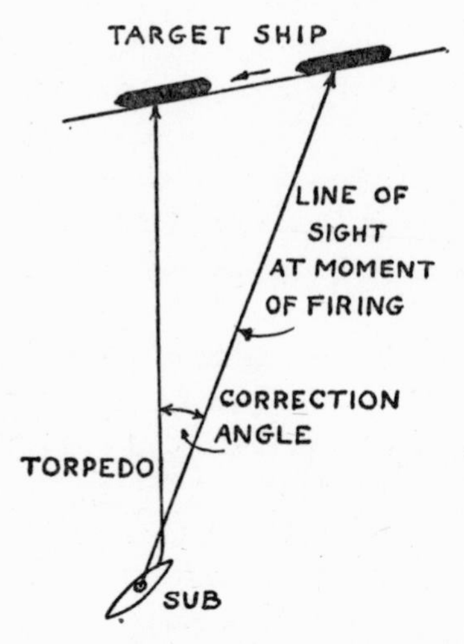

FIGURE 18. *Method of Aiming a Torpedo at a Moving Vessel*

operated in the control room. This heading is kept constant till the moment of firing. The captain's success as a marksman depends upon his skill in making accurate estimates and computations at high speed, often while under enemy fire. When the target is important it is common practice to fire a "spread" of several torpedoes, which gives the same likelihood of a hit that a shotgun gives a hunter.

The moment the torpedo is released its impulse bubble gives the sub's position to the enemy. It is then the captain's job to get his boat down and away, changing course and depth constantly so as to confuse his pursuers. If the enemy patrol is too thick he will proba-

FIGURE 19. *Scene in the Torpedo Room*

bly have to stop his motors and drift, taking whatever beating the depth charges give him. Sometimes he can give the impression that he is done for by ejecting fuel oil or bits of woodwork from toilet or torpedo tubes, and thus stop further attack. All the while, his men are listening intently for the sounds of propellers above, so as to give him an idea of which way to run.

It is during this critical time that the captain is most thankful for his habit of quick, accurate decisions and the smooth co-operation of the men he commands.

Sometimes a sub must lie low for many hours, while the crew nerves itself for the cataclysmic wrench of explosions close by. The depth charge drives a heavy pressure wave in all directions but expends most of its force in a cone upward. If the sub is in that cone its chances are poor. The explosions usually give the ship such a wrench that light filaments are broken and darkness is sent through the ship. Essential pipe lines may be smashed or the hull plates sprung. When such a catastrophe overtakes him the captain must decide whether to surface (if he still can) and surrender, or whether to stay down and hope to outlive the attack, and then get away under cover of night. Many a commander has chosen the latter course and, by furious pumping and emergency repairs, has lived to limp home. A submarine nowadays is a tough animal to exterminate when its crew has a nerve the equal of its mechanical strength.

EMERGENCY DRILLS AND TRAINING

THE fundamental concept of naval training is to be prepared. Brilliant solutions on the spur of the moment are necessary, but they must be based on endless rehearsals beforehand of every conceivable accident. There is a standard procedure for all contingencies. The instruction book for sub crews states it this way:

"All hands are reminded that the successful handling of emergencies must depend upon the cool logical action of men who know their submarine and who have ingrained in them the basic actions demanded of them by each emergency. The cardinal principle of all damage control is: as quickly as possible prevent the spread of damage. Know what to do, when to do it, how to do it and why you do it."

The principal emergencies enumerated are: collision, fire, chlorine gas, abandon ship, and man overboard. For each, a detailed procedure is given. For instance, collision, which is a constant threat in enemy waters. If the submarine is on the surface with hatches open her case is desperate, for she may sink before the openings can be closed. It is nearly impossible to close a hatch or door with water rushing through it. The captain and every officer must seal up every possible compartment at top speed by securing bulkhead doors and hatches. When all undamaged rooms are isolated it can be learned over the telephone what sections of the ship are free of water and how many men are still alive. If the collision caught the ship unprepared it will probably have sunk. In hostile waters the situation must be dealt with entirely by the stricken crew. If blowing all undamaged tanks will not surface the vessel the men must be ordered to escape with their Momsen lungs, or else face death. In peacetime, in shallow water, a marker buoy can be sent up and rockets released to bring help.

Collision is often serious but not fatal, damaging superstructure or causing bad leaks. The decision then must be whether to come up and surrender, or to deliberately take the ship down to its grave. Whatever the occasion, crew skill and the officers' expert knowledge of hydrostatics will often bring the boat through. Over and over again U-boats have been blasted and crushed only to reappear safely in their home ports. But fighting in the Pacific far from home does not give the American subs much chance, once they are badly wounded.

Fire and man overboard are treated as for a surface ship, success being measured by the precision and promptness of the measures taken. The procedure against chlorine gas, especially, must be carried out with utmost speed. When salt water hits the sulphuric acid of the storage batteries a thick green gas pours out. A few breaths of it are certain death. At the first suspicion of chlorine the battery rooms are ordered sealed and the sub is promptly surfaced. If the enemy makes this impossible the boat must limp away as best she can.

Abandon ship on the surface calls for the same routine as for other vessels, except that there are no lifeboats or rafts, and the men must don life preservers, throw over deck gratings or anything else that will float, and consign themselves to the sea. Abandon ship while submerged is the most dreaded of all. There is only one way to do it—through a hatch by means of the Momsen lung. A compartment is chosen for the escape, and the crew and officers are isolated in it by closing all doors. Lungs are strapped on and a heavy shot of oxygen is released into the room from the emergency bottles on the walls. The sea valves are then opened as wide as possible and the compartment flooded. The water will rise till the pressure of the trapped air equals the sea pressure outside, and the men float on the surface. The hatch trunk or "skirt" reaches below this level, being designed to do so, and thus makes escape possible without the loss of air.

When pressure is equalized a man breathing

FIGURE 20. *Method of Escape from Sunken Submarine with Momsen Lung*

through his Momsen lung is ordered to duck into the skirt and with a pike pole release the hatch above. It will open of its own accord by the force of its spring hinges. This same man then releases a buoy on a line, which rises to the surface and gives the men a pathway of escape. The end of the line is secured below.

On order of the captain the first man to leave grips

his escape-lung mouthpiece between his teeth and closes off his nose with the clamp provided. Taking a few deep breaths from the lung (filled with pure oxygen sufficient for ninety minutes of breathing), he ducks under, enters the hatch trunk, and begins his ascent, using the buoy line as a guide. He must go up as slowly as possible, reducing the pressure gradually so as not to burst eardrums or lungs. When he finally reaches the surface he removes the mouthpiece and clamp and uses the lung as a life preserver. The others follow at intervals, until all are saved.

Up to the present time no emergency escapes have been made from a sunken submarine by lung, though a dramatic rescue was effected by the McCann diving chamber on the *Squalus,* to be related later. In wartime escape is most unlikely, though eventually we may hear that it has been achieved. Sink or swim is the slogan of the fighting submarine.

CHAPTER SIX

THE U.S. SUBMARINE SCHOOL AT NEW LONDON

At the present writing the United States Navy has perhaps 150 submarines in service and 100 more building or planned. The average number in their crews is fifty men, meaning that soon the service will have to have more than 12,000 trained men. Where and how are these sailors made ready for the most exacting duty of all?

Prior to 1916, the Navy taught its undersea men their jobs by shipping them as trainees on active subs —the slow, hard way. In July of that year, however, war looked so imminent that a school was established at New London, Connecticut, to give the prospects a massive dose of information in advance. Highly specialized courses were started, covering the technical trades peculiar to the "Diving Navy." The school has been running steadily ever since, and is now graduating large groups of enlisted men and officers every few weeks.

The morale and skill of the American submarine force are acknowledged to be the best in the world. It is so because of the extraordinary care with which men and equipment are prepared. We have never followed the desperate German system of rushing boats and crews out on a production basis but have proceeded slowly, a few craft and a few men at a time, continually testing, changing, improving, always requiring higher standards. Even now, in the war emergency, training is not abbreviated in the slightest degree. Meanwhile a major threat to German submarine warfare is that its U-boat personnel is largely half-trained, compelled often against its will to take up the work. There are reports from Berlin that men are being shanghaied into this dangerous service.

PRELIMINARY REQUIREMENTS

THE fundamental of American submarine success lies in the kind of men chosen for undersea duty. The requirements are as stiff as those for aviation; in some respects stiffer, for sub men must not only perform their duties perfectly, but must work together under conditions of extreme crowding and danger, and never show the strain. Officer and enlisted material is picked with utmost care by the heads of the school and is closely watched throughout the training period and beyond on active service. If a man falls short in any respect he is instantly transferred; even after embarkation he may be removed simply on the recommendation of his commanding officer.

To qualify, a candidate must be in perfect physical condition, with good eyes, acute hearing, good lungs and stomach, and free from throat trouble or nervous disorders of any sort. Temperamentally he must be steady and unexcitable, resourceful, honest, and dependable. He need not be brilliant, but he must be intelligent and possess good judgment; he must coordinate well and show initiative. Also, he must be a good mixer and enjoy constant association with his fellows. He must be mechanically adept, a good man with his hands, and he must have a natural aptitude for the principles of machines. These requirements seem so severe as to be scarcely attainable; yet the school is always swamped with applications for enrollment and carries a steady waiting list. Not more than 10 per cent of the acceptable applicants fail to graduate.

The reasons why so many men desire undersea duty are easily understood. It offers unmatched opportunity for freedom and initiative and gives every man the chance to act on his own responsibility. The submarine is the soloist of the Navy and its exploits are interesting, exciting, and hazardous. Crew units are small and associations intimate. Life on board, while confining, is comfortable, and the relation of the men to their officers is rather like the affectionate intimacy of a large family. Formality is dispensed with, but respect for authority is solidly maintained. Officers and men have constant opportunity to exercise special skills and to train themselves for still higher proficiency. Lastly (and according to the submarine men themselves, least important), the Diving Navy receives more pay. The officers get a 25 per cent increase in their base pay on qualifying, the men $10 to $30 a month more than similar ratings elsewhere.

Thus the life appeals especially to American pioneer spirit and ingenuity, and beckons to the many thousands of men not content to go along in the routine way. All branches of the Navy require superior men, but the submarine service gets the cream of them all.

Future sub officers are taken from Annapolis on graduation or from the fleet shortly after, and are picked from those who have shown special aptitude in mechanical and electrical-engineering subjects. There are always more applications than there are positions to be filled. Enlisted men are drawn from all branches of the service but preferably from the Navy's numerous trade schools spotted about the country. Since all positions on a submarine are filled by specialists the school prefers to act as a postgraduate institution, taking only the men who have had technical groundwork and "boot training" elsewhere. It saves time and shifts the weeding-out process to what might be called the primary grades. A candidate need not be a college or even a high-school graduate. Physical stamina, mechanical aptitude, and temperamental fitness are the criteria.

ENTRANCE TESTS

OFFICERS and men alike must pass certain basic tests before admission to the school. When a man "puts in" for submarine-school assignment his physical and mental records are considered first. If he seems to qualify, his commanding officer recommends his transfer to New London. When he gets there he is subjected to three tests: the physical, the psychological, and the physiological. The physical examination comes first; it establishes beyond question whether the candidate's body will be able to stand the strain. Defects which can be overlooked in other Navy services will bar a man from submarines. Imperfect heart or lungs, a high-strung nervous system, chronic minor ailments, even glasses may disbar him. He need not be a prize fighter but he must be tough and endurant.

Most interesting, and also most recent, is the mental-fitness test given at New London by a skilled psychiatrist. Its purpose is to establish the man's moral and emotional characteristics as they will show up under water. It is usually given at the same time as the physical and often the men do not know they are getting it. During a short conversational interview the doctor watches the candidate closely and asks him leading questions to bring out his attitude and mental history. Such things as instability, defective intelligence, confusion of mind, illogic, inability to add and subtract, indifference to moral standards, tendency to anger or moroseness, and lack of sincerity or honesty occasionally turn up, and quickly rule a man out. If the applicant is a borderline case he may be given a more thorough mental test. A significant point to the doctor is whether or not the man keeps his appointments on time and takes them seriously. As most of the neophytes are in their early twenties the doctor must differentiate between poor character and mere youthful exuberance. He rarely makes a mistake.

The psychological study does not end with a man's entrance; the doctor watches his charges constantly during their training and particularly at sea. The critical point, mentally, comes with the first dive. The doctor is always aboard the training sub when a batch of new men is taken down, studying his neophytes closely for signs of panic, claustrophobia, or the effects of pressure. The trainee who falls down anywhere along the line is minutely discussed with the school officers, and if he is felt to be a bad risk he is gently removed.

The physiological test, which all must take before entering the school, is a special one to determine whether a candidate can live comfortably under pressure. The air in a submerged submarine is always slightly compressed, and if escape is to be made by Momsen lung the pressure may be very great. Some men are unable to stand even a little pressure, suffering nosebleeds, headaches, and even ruptured eardrums with a few extra pounds per square inch. To test this in advance the prospects are placed in a steel chamber with an experienced observer and subjected to gradually increasing air pressure up to fifty pounds. If any show distress the run is stopped and the sufferers removed. Then, if physical check-up indicates a faulty structure of the nasal passages or any other physical barrier, the men are dropped.

The second part of the test is done in the famous escape tank which towers 138 feet above the submarine base. This is filled with water and is provided with four entrance locks at twelve, eighteen, fifty, and 100 feet below the surface. The candidates are provided with Momsen lungs and are instructed in their use; then they are taken to the first level and launched

FIGURE 21. *Using the Momsen Lung in Escape Tank*

into the water, where they cling to a rope and float slowly upward under the guidance of an instructor. The first two escape stages must be mastered before a man qualifies for submarine training.

Once the three preliminary tests are behind him the candidate is ready for the intensive curriculum which will make him an expert. The school now divides into two parts: one for officers, taught by officers of long practical experience, and one for enlisted men, taught mainly by chief petty officers who have spent their lives on submarines.

OFFICERS' SCHOOL

THIS is an intensive course in every branch of submarine technique and is mainly of an advanced engineering nature. It qualifies the student for submarine duty in a subordinate capacity and includes instruction in design, construction, operation and maintenance, and in the theory of approach and attack. It also includes special lectures in commissary and supply, in medical treatment and first aid. The work is further specialized into engineering, torpedo, and communication departments in which the officers learn a particular branch which they wish to follow later.

The school is provided with large classrooms and a number of laboratories where the mechanics of the submarine are exhaustively studied. There are setups for working out typical attack problems with an actual periscope and miniature ship on the horizon. In addition there is a fleet of Class O submarines based at the school, in which constant practice trips are made. Here the students get experience in managing every part of a sub in actual running and diving operations, and attacks are simulated on coastwise shipping in Long Island Sound.

Much of the work is highly confidential, since the students are taught the use of the latest fire-control and listening and signaling apparatus. All through the course great stress is laid on good fellowship and on the independent judgment which the officer will constantly have to exercise on his future job.

ENLISTED MEN'S SCHOOL

This is the counterpart of the officers' school, except that emphasis is laid on the artisan side of submarine technique more than on the theoretical. Nevertheless, the men must have a solid grounding in fundamental principles. On the first day the class listens to a "fight talk" from a high-ranking officer who lays down the law and inculcates at once the high spirit of pride and devotion which must be every man's guiding light. The trainees are then given a notebook of general information which opens with this statement:

"All Hands Are Informed: That the submarine service expects every man aboard from the captain on down to know his boat from the top of the mast to the keel. Knowledge of the entire boat is demanded, not just that required within a particular department or line of work.

"That the hazardous nature of submarine operations demands from all detailed knowledge of construction, minute care in operation, and the highest attainable standard of attention to duty. . . . That each man on a submarine will be given responsibility far exceeding that on any other type of naval vessel."

With this vigorous preamble the neophyte is

launched into the hardest grind of book study and laboratory exercise he has ever met with in his life. His work is divided into week-long units, with two or three written and oral examinations in the course of each. During it all he must keep up a notebook, with lecture notes and careful sketches, which is inspected frequently by an instructor.

Study begins with the simplest fundamentals and works toward the complicated techniques of diving, engineering, and electrical operation. After a short time the student begins to take trips on the O-boats, during which he makes repeated dives. On these training trips he actually runs some part of the submarine himself, under the watchful eye of an old hand who prevents him from making any fatal mistakes. Every form of maneuver is practiced, including gunnery and the firing of (harmless) torpedoes. Sometimes the torpedoes themselves are not released, but, instead, slugs of water to represent them.

In the laboratories ashore the various parts of a submarine are displayed as a whole or in cutaway form. There is a complete set of storage batteries with switchboard and testing instruments; a diesel engine; a room filled with torpedoes and their component parts. The intricate piping systems of a sub are laid out on a long wall in diagrammatic form with valves, tanks, and accessories. In one laboratory a "mock-up" of the control room is mounted on a pivot and can be "dived" like a real boat. Each day a group of students goes aboard it and carries out the whole operation of submerging, taking orders from instructors standing near by. A miniature sub on the wall shows the actual position of the ship as the men manipulate the valves, and demonstrates their mistakes.

Classroom work consists of lectures, keeping detailed notes, and working practical problems in operation. In stiffness the course is the equivalent of college work.

When the "basic submarine course" is completed the men begin to specialize. Some go to the diesel course; some to the battery, gyro, or radio courses; others go to the special classes in underwater signaling, torpedo firing, etc. No man gets through who does not keep up in the "basic" and some specialty as well. The only exceptions are the few, like cooks and messboys, who bring their specialties with them.

The courses go on full blast six days a week, and a full day on Sundays is contemplated soon. A typical student day begins at 6:15 A.M., or 0615 as the Navy has it, and proceeds as follows:

0615—Reveille
0630—Men dressed, beds made, ready for inspection
0630—Breakfast
0740—Quarters, followed by drill and calisthenics
0800—Classes
1130—Lunch
1245—Classes again (or laboratory or ship duty)
1545—School ends for the day
1600 (4 o'clock)—Liberty begins for men not on watch. Recreation for those remaining on station

1750—Supper. Recreation in the evening (movies, bowling, pistol shooting, games, reading)
2145—Bedtime
2200 (10 o'clock)—Lights out

It is a pretty crowded day of sixteen hours, and the men work hard and play hard during every minute of it. But their spirit is top-notch. The course is so short that no one can afford to dally. If he does, and falls behind, he must make up with night study, or else get transferred back whence he came. But there is rarely a man who does not do his utmost to keep up. The doctor has weeded out the drones at the start. The few who fail on the way through are men who, try as they may, cannot make the grade.

FIGURE 22. *The Twin Dolphins Insignia*

When the course is over, the men graduate with diplomas. But their novitiate has only begun. Now come weeks and months on actual submarine duty before they become "qualified submarine men" entitled to wear the coveted gilt insignia of the twin dolphins on their chests. There is no fixed length of time for qualifying. When a submarine crew member thinks he is ready he asks his commanding officer for permission to take the final examination. This is in the form of a combined oral and written test prescribed by the Navy Department and given by the captain himself. Passing it depends on the skipper's recommendation as to the man's all-around qualifications as well as his technical knowledge.

Thus are the men of the submarine service groomed for actual duty in peace and war. Few once qualifying ever transfer into any other branch. They will tell you that it is the best of all duties, and the fact that submarines are admittedly dangerous makes no difference to them at all. They are comfortably fatalistic. "When the spot of ocean with my number on it comes up," they say, "well, it comes up; that's all." The prospects of diversified and exciting duty are too good to leave room for fear. The submarine is a "weapon of opportunity," and there is nothing like the kick a man gets when the pressure of his fingers on some lever or valve plays a part in sinking an enemy ship.

Our Navy's subs are large, oceangoing vessels now, and an enlisted man's billet on one of them means front-line fighting for the duration. Every time a new boat is commissioned some of these newly qualified specialists are signed on. In general the school supplies a skeleton crew for every added ship, filling the less important positions with the lesser trained, and binding them together with a sprinkling of veterans taken from older subs.

The reason why our subs have hung up so fine a record in the Pacific—and everywhere else—is that they are manned by experts whose training has been a matter of thoroughness rather than of speed.

CHAPTER SEVEN

RESCUE ON THE OCEAN FLOOR

One effect of World War I in the United States was to give our Navy a wholesome respect for submarine potentiality, and considerable numbers of new boats were planned and laid down. This interim crop was wisely designed to afford the heaviest possible striking power at the greatest attainable range. We did not expect ever to meet a surface enemy close to our own shores. Therefore our subs were built to operate over the huge expanses of Atlantic and Pacific from bases thousands of miles apart.

The development work on the new classes of American submarines involved great technical research; it also engendered endless trials and maneuvers to determine endurance and efficiency. Inherently the undersea boat is the most dangerous of fighting craft; the United States Navy was determined to make it as safe as possible. In this it has eminently succeeded. No other nation in the world has gone to such lengths nor achieved such high standards of crew protection and comfort.

AMERICAN SUBMARINE DISASTERS

THE loss of the *F-4* at Honolulu in 1915 first emphasized the importance of submarine rescue equipment in peacetime. After the war the *S-5* sank in the Delaware River. A spectacular rescue was performed by raising her by the stern, cutting a hole into her motor room with a blow torch and pulling the crew out through it. The two accidents showed the need for external means of aid. The air supply of a sunken sub may last her crew for thirty-six hours; after that they succumb to CO_2 poisoning. So the Navy fitted all its vessels with "salvage air connections" on the superstructure so that clean air could be blown in through hoses from the surface. Meanwhile the British sub *K-13* had been supplied with an experimental air-lock through which the crew could get free in case of accident. Eventually she foundered in fifty feet of water, and two men tried to use this lock. Both reached the surface, but one was killed by the pressure.

Then came two American disasters close together, teaching lessons which were responsible for all modern safety techniques. The first was the sinking of the *S-51* on a September night in 1925 in Block Island Sound. Proceeding on the surface with conning tower and hatches open she was run down and crushed by the coastwise steamer *City of Rome*. She sank in two minutes, spewing nine men into the sea. The remaining twenty-eight men below did not even have a chance to close bulkhead doors but drowned at their posts. The *S-51* was flooded throughout, and salvage officers were unable to blow her out sufficiently to obtain positive buoyancy. Raising her took nine months and was accomplished at great risk and expense with pontoons. The importance of better compartmentation was thoroughly demonstrated.

The *S-4* went down off Provincetown, Massachusetts, in December two years later, sunk by her attending destroyer when she surfaced unexpectedly just at dusk. She reached bottom in 160 feet of water, and tapping told the rescue vessels that there was life both forward and aft. The terrible tragedy enacted in the next two days was the Navy's worst. A severe storm was rising. Salvage officers had the choice of blowing her ballast tanks clear and raising her with the living still aboard, or of supplying breathing air by hose to hold them till the storm had passed. They could not do both at the same time, as sufficient compressed air was not available at short notice. Deciding that the large group of men aft were too weak to be saved by fresh air alone the officers gambled on raising the ship by blowing her tanks—and failed. The center compartment had been ruptured.

In the precious time thus lost the seas increased so much that a diver, trying to hook an air line to the forward torpedo room, nearly lost his life. The further delay in rescuing him ended all attempts at salvage for two days. When the storm finally abated and air was got down the last surviving men were dead. The entire crew of forty lost their lives—not through human failure, but because the details of the salvage air connections and other rescue devices were inadequate.

MODERN RESCUE TECHNIQUE

THE loss of the *S-4* emphasized the need of speed. Many hours had been sacrificed that December night dragging a grapnel to locate the ship before the first diver could go down. The tragedy also indicated that means should be provided for individual escape should outside aid fail to come quickly enough. As a result the *S-4*, when finally salvaged, was used as an experimental laboratory to develop new equipment.

Great advances came quickly. Oxygen tanks and cans of CO_2 absorbent were supplied to all submarines; emergency lighting circuits and flashlights were installed; emergency food rations were provided; the watertight doors between compartments were made quick-closing; communication systems were improved. Most important of all, each ship was fitted with a tube for firing smoke rockets to the surface and with marker buoys to be released upward at the end of cables. These carried with them telephone lines for direct communication with the surface. At the same time an emergency technique was developed for abandoning ship, as described in Chapter Five.

Ashore a deep-sea diving school was established in Washington to train divers to work under great pressure. A group of Navy doctors began an exhaustive study of the body's response to high pressure, working out tables of safe times to be spent under water at various depths, as well as schedules for recompression intervals necessary to prevent a diver's getting the bends. A significant discovery was that nitrogen under excessive pressures caused not only the bends but had a narcotic effect as well, rendering the diver childish and unable to execute even the simplest orders. The result was the "helium hat," or helmet supplied with helium gas instead of the nitrogen found in ordinary air. Helium affected a man's vocal chords but left his brain untouched.

At the same time Lieutenant Charles B. Momsen, Annapolis, 1920, began experimenting on the *S-4* with an underwater breathing apparatus to help men escape from sunken boats. The Momsen lung, which resulted, is probably the greatest single advance in submarine safety. It consists of a breathing mask strapped across the mouth, a nose clamp to prevent nasal breathing, and a rubber chamber filled with pure oxygen and connected to the mask through valves. The important feature is that it provides a closed system, the wearer exhaling back into the chamber through a canister of CO_2 absorbent. Thus there is no danger of water getting into the lungs through jammed valves. The whole apparatus is strapped on tightly, and the man can, if he rises slowly enough to avoid the bends, save himself from depths of at least 150 feet. During the whole development, Momsen made all the trials himself, and for this display of courage he received the Distinguished Service Medal.

The danger that submarine disasters might occur in water too deep for the lung set Lieutenant Allan R. McCann to work on a modern version of the diving bell, first made practical by Dr. Edmund Halley, discoverer of the famous comet. The McCann rescue

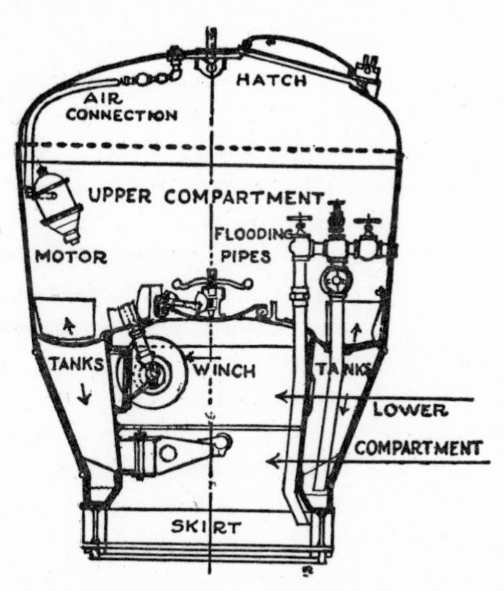

FIGURE 23. *The McCann Submarine Rescue Chamber*

chamber, as finally developed, is a steel tank eight feet in diameter and ten feet high, divided into upper and lower compartments by a watertight hatch. The lower "skirt" is finished off smooth to fit with a rubber gasket on a special escape hatch on the submarine, to which it is fastened down by bolts on arrival. In use the chamber is swung down into the water by a cable and reels itself down on a wire guide line previously made fast to the sub by a diver. Ballast tanks give the chamber neutral buoyancy to overcome the lift of the air inside. A crew of two men operate it, sitting in the brilliantly lighted upper compartment adjusting buoyancy with compressed air from the ship above. Once in contact with the submarine the crew of the chamber blows the water from the lower compartment, exhausts the air to the sub's internal pressure, then climbs down and opens the hatch so that the trapped men can climb up into the bell. Development work on this was extremely hazardous, and again the inventor insisted on taking all the experimental risks. He and his assistants were rewarded with special promotions. Today there are eleven rescue chambers spotted along our coasts, and every submarine in the service has at least two hatches specially fitted to receive them.

A highly organized rescue squadron is now maintained on both coasts, centering in the East around the salvage vessel *Falcon,* based at New London. Besides her crew of divers there are many more who are expert in this work stationed in every naval district. Doctors and other specialists in salvage are available to be flown to the scene of a disaster. For eleven years after the *S-4* went down there was not a single submarine accident which resulted in loss of life. Then, on the eve of the new war came the vital test. After the Navy had made 100,000 dives without a hitch, the *U.S.S. Squalus* sank on her trials off Portsmouth, New Hampshire, in 1939, with a loss of twenty-six men.

RESCUE OF THE SQUALUS'S *CREW*

THE *Squalus* was the Navy's newest, a 310-foot giant of 1,500 tons. She had made eighteen successful trial dives, and this was the last of her preliminary trials. A rapid sketch of the affair is given here to show how the Navy works in emergency and to demonstrate how even the finest preparations cannot remove all the natural hazards of the sea. For this information I am indebted to a Boston reporter, Nat A. Barrows, who published an eye-witness account of the rescue which is a classic.

Everything was shipshape that May morning when Lieutenant Naquin and his crew of fifty-seven officers and men and one civilian observer took the boat out into the Atlantic for a high-speed dive. In the control room, to which he had descended after ordering the ship to rig for diving, he was surrounded by a crack group, and from end to end every man knew his job, having been through hundreds of dives before. Naquin gave the order, "Stand by to dive!" with complete confidence.

As each operation of securing the machinery and closing the hull openings was completed the red lights on the "Christmas Tree" before Naquin were replaced by green. Lieutenant Doyle, the diving officer, presently reported: "Pressure in the boat. Green board, sir." The captain nodded; levers were moved and the ballast tanks began to fill. Naquin and every man in the control room checked that green board. The depth gauges moved up. The *Squalus* was on her way down —in record time.

At fifty feet, Preble, the civilian observer, called out "Mark!" and punched his stop watch. Doyle leveled off. The crash dive was over. Then, as the skipper started to congratulate his men a terrified voice rang in the telephone receivers clamped to the yeoman's ears in the control room. In the engine room a man was yelling: "Take her up! The inductions are open!" The after part of the ship was flooding. Naquin glanced at the "Christmas Tree." It was still green. There had been a double failure: inductions had opened and the indicators had not showed it.

There was no panic. The skipper snapped out orders to blow tanks, up diving planes, and surface. The crew responded instantly. The *Squalus* raised herself slightly, hesitated, then tilted slowly backward, and slipped helplessly to the bottom. The depth gauges steadied at last at 240 feet.

In every compartment men rushed to close watertight doors. What happened in the engine room and spaces aft is not known. Long afterward it became evident that the twenty-six men there struggled desperately to get through into the torpedo room astern and close the bulkhead behind them—and failed. There were eight others on duty in the battery room aft of the control room. When the flood began they quickly closed the engine-room door, and thought they were safe. But the large ventilating ducts, cross-connected to the air-induction lines, spouted water, and the battery room began to fill. The steep angle of the stricken ship as she foundered threw these men flat, and they slid back into the water. Thrashing and clutching at bunks they pulled themselves uphill and wriggled through the door into the control room just as the men there swung it shut. At this moment all lights went out.

Telephoning forward Naquin found everything dry there, except that the batteries were flooded and chlorine was seeping through the floor. He ordered this room isolated at once. Thirty-three men were safe so far. There was no response to calls aft and no way to know whether any had survived to gain the end compartment. The situation was serious, for 240 feet was at the extreme depth limit for salvage diving.

Naquin ordered the combination smoke bomb and telephone buoy released forward; then he had all hands break out and keep near them the Momsen lungs. He hated to think of using them but it might be necessary. Then he sat down to wait, in the dark. The emergency lighting circuit had failed with the battery, and flashlights were too precious to use until later.

Upon diving that morning the *Squalus* had sent her routine radio message to the Navy Yard, giving her position and time of starting down. When no resurfacing message had been received after two hours Admiral Cole, the Commandant, knew there was trouble. Telephoning New London and Washington to stand by for a rescue call he sent the submarine *Sculpin* out to look for her sister ship. At six minutes past one she picked up the marker buoy and got into communication with Naquin below. The two officers were close friends. Lieutenant Commander Wilkin, on the surface, said a few words of comfort. Before Naquin could give him any details a heavy wave jerked the buoy upward and tore it loose from the *Squalus,* telephone line and all. The ship was marooned.

Coolly, Naquin divided his men into watches, assigned them the arduous duty of striking out messages on the sub's hull with sledge hammers. It was his only way of communicating, since the oscillator had gone out with the batteries. On the surface the *Sculpin,* making the best possible use of her underwater receivers, planted buoys all around the apparent position of the wreck. But accurate location at that depth was impossible. Below, Naquin fed his crew from the emergency stores and ordered all but the signal watch to lie flat and keep quiet—the best way to conserve air and maintain strength. The temperature of the water outside the hull was twenty-six degrees.

The disaster call went out at one o'clock. In New London, the *Falcon* rushed her crew aboard, picked up her rescue chamber, and headed for the sea. In New York, McCann himself boarded a plane with twelve of his best divers, while in Washington Momsen and two doctors and a master diver took to the air in another. Admiral Cole hurried to the scene on the tug *Penacook;* the cruiser *Brooklyn* and many other vessels converged from various ports, bringing supplies and rescue gear of all kinds. Reporters by the hundreds grabbed planes and cars and headed for Portsmouth.

The wives and families of many *Squalus* men hastened to follow.

Shortly after 3:00 P. M. the *Penacook* arrived and began dragging for the *Squalus* with a grapnel; until she was found and a line had been dropped to her deck no diving could be attempted. Not until 7:10 did the grapnel catch. At nine the first plane, with Momsen and the doctors, roared down at the Navy Yard. The second, bringing McCann and the divers, was forced down in Rhode Island by fog, whence the party started off through the thick night by car. The exciting trip over roads cleared by the police of three states did not end till three in the morning. And not until 4:30 did the *Falcon,* shuddering under every ounce of steam she could put on, heave in sight and join the growing rescue fleet over the *Squalus.* Though working at utmost speed the Navy had consumed twenty hours in assembling its salvage crews.

During all that time Naquin and his men had huddled in blankets in total darkness, lying in each other's arms to stave off the dreadful cold. But they did not feel alone. A heartening stream of Morse signals had been coming to them from the *Sculpin's* oscillator, whining loudly through the water and the *Squalus's* hull, and keeping them informed of every move on the surface. For their part the trapped men had laboriously answered with their sledge hammers—one blow for a dot, two for a dash. So deadening was the thick blanket of water that every message had to be repeated three times, till the weakened men were almost exhausted. Detail after detail they had sent, till those above were dreadfully aware of the creeping cold, the nausea, and coma that were gradually overtaking the waiting crew. Nor was the vigil over when the *Falcon* finally arrived. She must anchor securely before the divers could go down.

FIGURE 24. *The U. S. Submarine Rescue Ship* Falcon

Naquin's steady nerve kept up the morale so well that most of the men slept. He himself remained awake; he and Doyle talked in low tones and discussed the meaning of the confused propeller sounds which came down from above. Both recognized the *Falcon* as she jockeyed for position, lost her hold in the rough sea, and anchored again—four times.

The commotion went on so long without explanation that finally Naquin released a smoke rocket to see what was wrong. At once the *Falcon* responded with a sharp message on her oscillator:

"Am mooring over you. Do not release any more smoke rockets. What was meaning of last smoke rocket?"

"No sound. Fired red to get contact," the *Squalus's* men tapped out weakly. Nerves all round were at hair-trigger tension.

At length the *Falcon's* last anchor bit the muddy bottom and held; the east wind dropped, and the sun blazed out over a sea that suddenly took on the polish of flexible glass. A cheer went up from all hands. Shortly after ten diver Sibitzky, a giant in rubber suit and helmet, clattered to the *Squalus's* foredeck and felt around. Luck was with him; the forward escape hatch was near by. Five minutes later his job was accomplished: the downhaul cable for the rescue chamber was securely shackled to the hatch.

On the *Falcon's* deck McCann stood eagerly awaiting the next act in the drama—the first actual rescue of marooned men by his diving chamber. No time was lost. With its numerous air and service lines clear, the chamber was lifted and swung down into the water. Inside were Mihalowski and Harman, both divers of long experience who had gone through many tests with the chamber. McCann picked up his telephone and ordered the descent to begin.

Mihalowski opened a valve, and compressed air set the winch motor in motion. The downhaul cable began to come in, pulling the chamber foot by foot into the sea. Harman watched the gauges and adjusted the ballast tanks to give slight positive buoyancy and keep the chamber upright. In a few minutes they bumped gently on the *Squalus's* deck. Unwatering the skirt and dropping its air pressure to normal, Mihalowski climbed down and secured the safety bolts around the rescue hatch. Directly below ten exhausted men listened eagerly. It was almost worth the suffering to know that they would be the first ever rescued by this modern diving bell.

Quickly twirling the hatch release wheel, Mihalowski saw the cover spring back. He dropped down the escape trunk, opened the lower door, and looked in. Below, a group of upturned faces lighted in the glimmer of his flashlight.

"Hello," the diver said. "Here we are." It was half-past twelve. Preble and five others were boosted into the upper compartment of the chamber. Meanwhile Mihalowski handed down hot coffee and blew fresh air into the torpedo room. In fifteen minutes preparations were complete. The routine was reversed—the hatches were closed, the skirt blown to outside pressure and flooded, the chamber gently cut loose. Putting on a little reserve buoyancy the operators eased it with its eight passengers toward the surface, unreeling the downhaul cable as they went. At 1:33 P. M., twenty-nine hours after the accident, the first group of rescued men were lifted over the *Falcon's* side and helped below for stimulants and rest.

By six that night three trips had been completed successfully; only Naquin and seven men were still in the submarine. The skipper was the last man to climb through the hatch and begin the ascent—at a little after eight. On the surface it was dark. Suddenly McCann heard a cry over the telephone. The chamber was stuck at 160 feet. It would not move, either up or down. There was a rapid consultation on the *Falcon,* an exchange of questions and answers with the men below. Only one solution was possible: to drop the chamber to the bottom, send down a diver to cut the fouled wire, then haul the bell up by the thin "preventer wire" attached to its top. This wire was intended only for a guide. It would probably not hold.

The men in the chamber coolly followed orders, took on ballast, and sank to the ocean floor. As quickly as was humanly possible a diver dropped to the submarine and cut the tangled downhaul. Then the *Falcon* began very slowly to take the chamber up by the thin wire that remained. When twenty feet of this had come over the rail a frayed end suddenly slipped into view. Only a single strand of the cable was left.

Again hurried orders were given and the chamber dropped to the bottom. Naquin and his comrades sat with tight lips. They had no idea what the chances were. On the *Falcon* a second diver was hurriedly dressed and dropped down the preventer wire to the bell, hoping to reeve in a new cable. But he was no sooner down than his life lines fouled in the frayed ends above him; he was in desperate trouble. It took his last ounce of strength under the 109 pounds of pressure to get himself free. The moment he was up a third diver descended and worked for half an hour to shackle a new wire to the chamber. But his life lines fouled also. He was hauled up unconscious.

The chamber had now been submerged for four hours, and the strain was telling on its occupants. Admiral Cole made the final decision to haul it up on its own damaged wire. McCann had not slept for thirty-six hours; Naquin had been awake for nearly two days. But neither man lost his head. While the occupants of the rescue chamber sang and told stories, the men on deck began to haul in, a few inches at a time, avoiding jerks and slack with breathless care. Foot after foot came in, while McCann above and Mihalowski below jockeyed the weight of the bell to keep an even strain. And at last the broken section of cable was over the rail and only good wire ran below. At one o'clock in the morning, in the brilliant glare of floodlights and amidst the cheers of every man in the salvage fleet, the chamber broke the surface and the drama was over.

McCann's invention had had its baptism and was soon celebrated around the world. A week later the British submarine *Thetis* sank in the Mersey and virtually all were drowned. There was no rescue chamber in England, and all were drowned. A few days later the French boat *Phenix* went down in the China Sea, killing seventy-seven more. This was indeed tragic emphasis on the necessity for highly organized salvage procedure, such as the United States alone had mastered.

The raising of the *Squalus* with her burden of dead took nearly four months to accomplish. It required 640 dives, a majority of them at extreme depth. The "helium hat," which Admiral Cole had not dared to experiment with during the rescue, was put into service and undoubtedly saved many divers' lives. When the sub's battered hull finally rested in drydock an engineering board minutely examined the air-induction valves and their operating machinery inside; they were all in perfect working order. A court of inquiry later reviewed every shred of evidence and every word of survivors' testimony and decided that the *Squalus* had gone down for causes largely unknown. Failure had apparently been mechanical, but there was a mysterious element never to be solved: hand valves in the engine room that should have closed off the induction lines were found open. The men whose duty it had been to operate them were dead. Had it been carelessness—or sabotage? Some who noted the quick succession of submarine disasters around the world that May thought it must be the latter. No one will ever know.

Of the thirty-three survivors not one asked for transfer from the Diving Navy. All hands, including the two Filipino messboys, were anxious to sign on again with the first ship they could get. And a year later the *Squalus,* refitted and renamed the *Sailfish,* was ready for sea again. What she has accomplished since in the Pacific will be told further on.

CHAPTER EIGHT

GERMANY STRIKES AGAIN: 1939-40

An analysis of the present submarine war is necessarily incomplete since many of the details are still shrouded in mystery. However, enough data is available to give a substantial outline of what has happened and a reasonable prophecy of what is in store. At the moment of writing, June, 1942, the German submarine has the same kind of strangle hold on United States coastwise shipping that it had upon Britain's life lines in 1917. The rate of sinkings is not so great in tonnage per month, but it is enough to throw the maritime balance of power to the enemy. To stall off Allied victory—to drag on the war indefinitely—all Germany needs to do is to sink and sink, anywhere, anyhow, anything that carries ocean cargo. All the shipping at present available is not enough to move the needed supplies to the battle fronts of the world; even the huge building program has not made up the deficiency. As long as the U-boat can keep the gap unfilled, Hitler's defeat will be a well-nigh impossible task.

Submarine warfare may be beaten in two ways: either by building tonnage so fast that the losses become insignificant in comparison to the gain; or by so greatly improving the antisubmarine defense that the sinkings themselves become insignificant. The latter policy won the battle of 1917–18, and it has virtually won the Battle of the Atlantic. But for various reasons we have not yet been able to employ it in the Battle of America. At the moment we are like a man whose house is on fire and who tries to build additions to the house rather than call the fire department.

The submarine can be beaten. It has found no startling new methods of attack; in fact, it has gone back to the easy-pickings-on-undefended-merchantmen idea of 1915 and 1916. We are experiencing the same rude treatment now that the British did when submarine warfare was new, but with the disadvantage that there is no friendly neutral giant to hold U-boat depredations down with diplomatic threats. To date we have not done so well with our coastal problem as the British did with theirs.

UNPREPAREDNESS

THE situation that has obtained since 1939 might have been avoided, so far as submarines are concerned, if proper precautions had been taken in advance. If the democratic nations had built great numbers of patrol craft—subchasers, destroyers and cruisers, blimps and scouting planes—as well as battleships, the submarine war could have been resumed *where it was dropped in 1918.* If we had acquired a great merchant marine; if we had so arranged our internal economy that coastal war could not affect vital supplies of oil and rubber and aluminum; if, indeed, we had joined together in suppressing Hitler in embryo, we should not have had a war to win at all. But these ifs are idle now; at best they are finger posts to be heeded the next time.

A great deal has been said about the stupidity of German psychology. Most of such talk is poppycock. The Nazis understood the minds and hearts of the democracies so well that they were able to plan and prepare for a new war under their very noses without exciting alarm. Indeed, the will of the free peoples to a better life assisted Hitler by softening his future opponents and by causing them to deny the fact that there could still be bad men in the world. Nazi strategists played this gullibility for all it was worth.

In 1935, they made a great gesture of co-operation by signing the Anglo-German Naval Treaty, which limited the German fleet to 35 per cent of Britain's sea strength—*in all types of vessels but submarines.* In these Ambassador von Ribbentrop chiseled out a figure of 45 per cent, without causing alarm. To allay any slight suspicion, he signed in the following year a protocol binding the Reich to the London Naval Treaty of 1930, in which the United States, Great Britain, France, and Japan had reaffirmed the principle that merchantmen must not be sunk without warning. And finally, on the threshold of Munich in 1939, the German Government notified the world of her intention to build her submarine fleet up to full parity with Britain. Still there was no official alarm.

In "There Shall Be No Night," Robert E. Sherwood

has a Nazi official say that Germany will get away with her plans for world conquest because they are so fantastic that no one will take them seriously. But nothing in history is so fantastic as the blindness of the world's statesmen in regard to the German submarine policy. Here was the resurgence of the one weapon that had struck terror to the heart of the British Empire, yet nothing was done to prevent its use again. Naval men did not even prepare properly to fight the submarine as they had fought it before.

For two years prior to the outbreak of war in 1939 British merchant captains were being carefully trained in the theory and execution of convoy maneuvers. Yet the vessels that were fundamental to convoy success were omitted from the building programs. In 1918, the Allies had barely beaten the submarine with a total of nearly 700 destroyers, not to mention hundreds of other patrol ships. In 1939, England had 175, many of them old ships. The United States was in similar case. All the great navies were groaning under the load of vast battleship construction instead. All except Nazi Germany. Hitler had said: "Big ships are things that only the plutocracies can afford." For years he had been busy making up the 55 per cent deficiency in submarines by building U-boat parts on the sly. The cynical proposal to reach parity with the British was a statement of accomplishment, not of intent.

Yet nobody knew. The U-boat hung like an evil shadow under the waters of the seven seas—and went unnoticed. The certain answer to it was understood but not provided. World naval strategy was buried in the same coffin as the Battle of Jutland. The two were corpses together, but neither dreamed that it was dead.

From Hitler's point of view the prospects of 1939 were bright. Even if his opponents had been awake there would at least have been an even chance for the new U-boats to win. German naval men had learned their submarine lessons well. Their undersea fleet was well diversified. Not only did they possess large vessels for long-range work, but several smaller types for inshore duty, including a 250-ton "minnow" with a radius of 1,200 miles. On the negative side, they were aware that convoy was not a complete answer to submarine attack. The depth charge was troublesome but not always fatal. Moreoever, there was a new cure for surface molestation in the use of the airplane with a long-distance radio link to the U-boats. Sinkings had been hit or miss before; now they could be planned in advance.

The German Navy knew well that it could not win a decisive submarine victory along the lines of former defeat. As long as the U-boats remained bottled up in the North Sea they would have only a nuisance value. They must have bases on the open Atlantic. Therefore, the plan was clear: to hold the U-boats in reserve while the army and the air force overcame France and Norway, then to spring suddenly at the throat of England *from the west* and finish her off.

Thus Hitler's main submarine campaign against Britain began with the seizure of Denmark and Norway and the drive into the Low Countries, culminating in the French armistice of June, 1940. In a miraculous series of lightning coups he not only subjugated six nations but obtained better than 1,000 miles of coast line bordering directly on the Atlantic. The real U-boat war could now begin.

From the invasion of Poland on, the conflict has divided itself into four clean-cut phases, in each of which the submarine has driven the sinking rate up until the Allies, becoming desperate, have applied countermeasures strong enough to force it down again. These phases may be designated as follows:

1. The Battle for Position: September, 1939, to Dunkirk.
2. The Battle of the Atlantic, I: Summer, 1940, to April, 1941.
3. The Battle of the Atlantic, II: Spring, 1941, to Spring, 1942.
4. The Battle of America: Spring, 1942—?

The accompanying graph shows how the tonnage losses per month have fluctuated in response to submarine action and counteraction. The present trend of the curve should be downward before long. Whether there will be a fifth phase, or more, depends upon factors beyond prophecy.

THE BATTLE FOR POSITION

WHEN hostilities opened on September 1, 1939, Hitler had an embarrassment of military riches. Devoting himself to overrunning helpless Poland by land and air he allowed his U-boats to take up the fight exactly

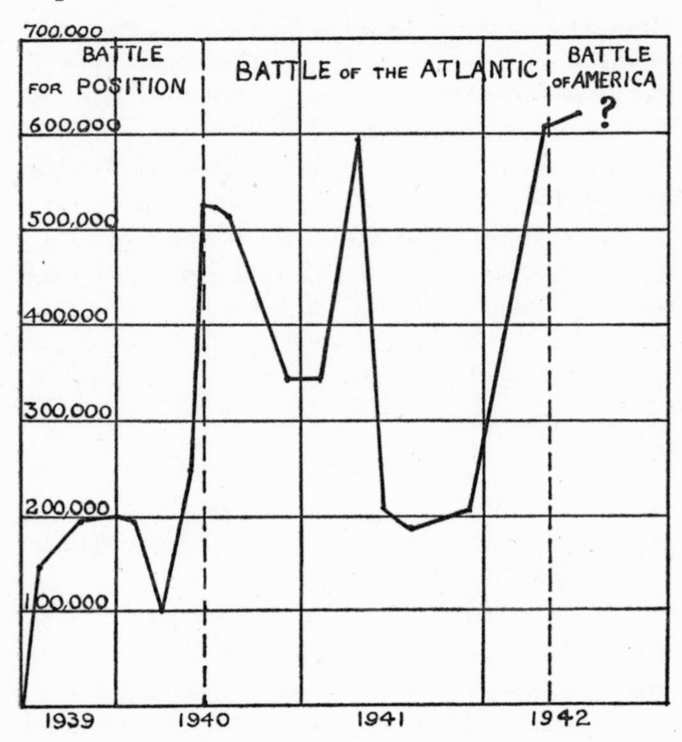

FIGURE 25. *Rate of Merchant Ship Sinkings, World War II*

as they had begun it twenty-five years before, with a general attack upon British naval units and single merchantmen. This was a carefully planned preliminary action to capitalize on his enemies' somnambulance and get a head start by the old-style method.

At that time Britain had a total merchant fleet of some 2,500 cargo vessels—over 6,000,000 tons in all. Easily 2,000 of these were at sea when war began, unarmed and helpless. The initial U-boat haul was therefore large. In the first two weeks thirty ships to a total of 140,000 tons were torpedoed. On top of that a lucky shot sank the aircraft carrier *Courageous* with 600 men. This was a new kind of prize; the disaster indicated that the fleet air arm was highly vulnerable. To be safe such a warship must have strong escort, with a consequent drain on cruisers and destroyers badly needed for other duty.

A few weeks later a lone sub commander made a daring raid on Scapa Flow at night and torpedoed the battleship *Royal Oak,* catching the British completely unprepared. The dreadnaught lay within the supposedly perfect protection of defense nets, booms, and mine fields. But the U-boat, waiting for high tide, sneaked in through them all and sent four torpedoes home. The ship foundered in a few minutes, taking 804 of her men to the bottom and sending a wave of rage and fear throughout England. An explanation was demanded by Parliament, and Lord Strabolgi, speaking for the government, admitted that Scapa Flow was not impregnable. The threat of submarines had been underestimated.

The psychological complexion of the new conflict was quickly set with the full use of the "war of nerves" —a touch Hitler had invented himself. Its opening gun was the sinking, on September 4, of the British liner *Athenia,* 200 miles west of Scotland. The 13,581-ton greyhound was heading west for Montreal and had no military significance. Of the 1,418 persons aboard 311 were Americans, three of them children. This new

Lusitania sank with forty-four persons lost, none of them United States citizens. However, a storm of indignation broke on both sides of the ocean, and many shook their fingers at Hitler and prophesied his early destruction.

The Führer calmly pulled a new one out of his bag by officially denying responsibility (although many survivors testified they had seen the U-boat's markings clearly) and suggesting that the British had done it themselves. This was, of course, utter nonsense and only increased international anger. But it had a deep purpose behind it. The *Athenia* affair was the first of a series of symbols; it was open notice to the world that the attack was to be against everybody and that dishonesty and deceit were to be used as boldly as other weapons. It was intended to disorganize and confuse, to strike fear and foreboding into the hearts of all people by threatening their security. It succeeded. Hitler intended to complete his lightning war within a year, and he knew that in a short war fright and disorganization are major forces.

A second example of the war of nerves came on October 5, when Grand Admiral Raeder notified the State Department in Washington that the American liner *Iroquois,* then sailing for the United States, was to be torpedoed by the British in a "second attempt to cast blame on the German Reich." The reaction was again violent. President Roosevelt denounced the warning as ridiculous, and the British Admiralty referred to the message as a proof of the Nazi "criminal mentality." Nevertheless, the United States Navy felt it necessary to send out destroyers to convoy the *Iroquois* into port. Hitler had got a rise out of both governments. They had called him a thug, as if to do so would somehow slay him. But the word only amused him. Meanwhile the anger, argument, and confusion created were as valuable to the Nazi cause as the torpedoing of the vessel would have been.

Such easy psychological success led to more brazen attempts still. The Nazis now accused the British of secretly arming merchant vessels in defiance of international law and used this as a complete justification for sinking everything without warning. In December, they hit the peak by publishing a blacklist of British and American liners which were claimed to be armed and therefore were classed as "warships." As a final flourish, they proposed to sink any vessel, American or otherwise, that submitted itself to British seizure and search in the Mediterranean.

An amazing new strategy was developing: to commit any desired atrocity in full daylight and then, with a bland smile, blame it on the victim. More amazing still, the trick succeeded. The submarine lent itself perfectly to this nefarious scheme, for it was never possible to be absolutely sure what sub fired a torpedo unless the attacker was caught—which it seldom was. The only satisfactory answer to such accusations would have been complete and stony silence. That is not a habit of free-speaking peoples. Angrily, they talked; talking, they argued; arguing, they doubted—and the war of nerves was on. Then, too, there was in America an important section of anti-British feeling, isolationism, and pro-Axis sympathy. In the hurly-burly of good American shouting, these elements could be mobilized too.

There is no doubt that the scheme succeeded; that it actually helped to delay American participation for two years, and so gave Hitler the opportunity to conquer all Europe. Propaganda was the "secret weapon" that the world had dreaded for so long.

ANTISUBMARINE MEASURES BEGUN

THE British were not long in adopting countermeasures against the U-boats. Convoy, already well rehearsed, was started in the first week of the war. Patrol, mine barrages, aerial scouting, and depth-charge attack were all set in motion at once. Organized along the successful lines of 1918, they soon began to show favorable results. By late fall it was reported that the tally of submarines sunk had reached several per week. In the line of offensive measures the well-tried blockade was established, and a new Ministry of Economic Warfare began the arduous task of bringing all neutral vessels into port and examining their cargoes.

Methods of submarine detection had not been neglected. A highly secret group of scientists was organized, known as the Antisubmarine Defense Investigation Committee, and soon they contributed an improved form of underwater range and direction finder based on the old Fessenden principle of reflected sound. But the new "Asdic," as it was called, was a great advance, for it achieved extreme range and sensitivity by the use of sound waves above the audible scale. Asdic had had its initial success in detecting the "pirate submarines" in the Spanish Civil War, and it now became the white hope of U-boat extermination. Deep secrecy enveloped the whole research, and still does. It is believed that in this one respect the United Nations have the distinct edge on Germany. The reflection principle has been adopted for radio plane detectors as well.

With Asdic installed on patrol vessels the British were considerably encouraged. By January, 1940, there was a definite drop in merchant sinkings, and it was

FIGURE 26. *Convoy*

believed that the peak of the submarine activity was passed. Nevertheless, the threat was not over. It was still impossible to tell whether the U-boats were being smashed, or whether they had merely been withdrawn for other duty. The truth lay half way between the two. In the spring of 1940, Hitler needed his undersea craft for something new that he was planning in the North Sea.

His submarines were stronger than ever, in numbers and in endurance. Hulls had been toughened; superstructures now carried armor. Also, the U-boat now had the benefit of a German improvement of the old hydrophone nearly equivalent to Asdic.

The ability of the new submarines to take a beating was well demonstrated by the experience of a British boat caught in the North Sea by a pack of Nazi destroyers and disabled, so that she had to sink to the bottom and lie "doggo" to throw off pursuit. The hunters hung around on the surface all day, dropping tons of explosives, while the Englishmen lay prone below to conserve air and insure silence. They remained that way for twenty-four hours, and passed the time laying bets on how soon and how close the next blast would come. At last, one charge made a near hit, shattering the lights and disabling the diesels and one electric motor, and causing serious leaks in the high-pressure air line. There in the dark the men wrapped their tools in sheets of rubber to avoid their telltale clank, and managed to stop the escape of the irreplaceable air. That night they blew tanks and came to the surface, ready to demolish their ship with explosives if the Germans were still there to capture them. But they were not, and the sub limped off on one motor, managed to radio for help, and got towed in.

GERMANY ACQUIRES SUB BASES

THE spring of 1940 seemed to augur well for British shipping. Sinkings were down to 100,000 tons a month—a level that had not been reached until two weeks before the Armistice in 1918. News had come that the Nazis were building a fleet of tiny 150-ton subs with crews of twenty men. This indicated that they were running dangerously short of U-boat material—quite likely considering how small was the surface navy from which to draw trained personnel. There were rumors of long-range cruiser submarines on the loose in the open Atlantic. These had been reported as far west as the Caribbean. And there was some corroboration for this in the signing of the inter-American "Declaration of Panama," on the previous October 4, declaring all waters within 300 miles of the American continents closed to foreign vessels of war. But on the whole, British shipping was getting through, and Hitler seemed to have been stopped both on land and sea.

Then on April 8 he suddenly launched an attack headlong through Denmark upon the coast of Norway. Even after he had established a bridgehead there the full import of this masterly move was not understood. Winston Churchill himself, then First Lord of the Admiralty, was able to say with perfect confidence: "Hitler's action . . . is as great a strategic and political error as that committed by Napoleon when he invaded Spain." Military opinion everywhere agreed.

To sustain an invasion over the 100-mile width of the Skagerrak under the guns of the British Navy was impossible. And Britain began demonstrating this by torpedoing transports right and left.

But the military pundits had forgotten the airplane. Not only did the Nazi hordes maintain their Scandinavian foothold but in one lightning stroke after another drove northward under a canopy of superior air power, and in less than three weeks had chased the English expeditionary force out of Norway altogether. In the breathless tragedy of the new conquest few realized what it was Hitler was after, and what he got: submarine bases at Trondheim and Namsos on the open North Atlantic.

And before his adversaries could catch up in their mental readjustments he was off again, this time into Holland and Belgium and France. In the holocaust of smoke and terror and spectacular courage that surrounded Dunkirk the Nazi strategy at last became plain: territory and bases! Bases for unrestricted U-boat warfare along the whole European coast from the Arctic Circle to Spain. All in one terrible month of May the evil genius of the Third Reich had executed, absolutely on schedule, the preliminary moves in a prearranged plan. Even then naval authorities on the opposing side did not realize the full magnitude of the disaster. The horror of France's fall obscured the major threat.

It was not long obscured. England was to be invaded at once, before the summer ended. But that was not all: she was to be caught in a pincer move from both land and sea. The German Navy, cruisers, submarines, and all, would move in from the south and west, while the army and air force piled in from the south, east, and north. Quietly Hitler played his carefully held

FIGURE 27. *Business End of a U-boat, Showing Cable Cutters*

trump card: he began to move knock-down submarines by rail to the French west coast. By this move all the highly organized old-style U-boat defenses were suddenly nullified. The Channel mine barrages were no good now. The patrols of the Heligoland Bight were ineffective, the successful controls of 1918 at last obsolete.

Hitler had circumvented them all. By fall he would be free to launch a major submarine thrust against convoys on the high seas. Nor was it to be a mere repetition of the dark days of 1917. Germany was at last the geographical equal of Britain.

CHAPTER NINE

THE BATTLE OF THE ATLANTIC

THE attitude of "Let Hitler start something, we'll show him!" which had been so popular in the spring of 1940, was all gone by midsummer. Before May was over the Nazis had established refueling points along the coast of Norway, and the reach of the U-boats into the Atlantic was thus enormously increased. Early fall saw major submarine bases in operation at Lorient and Brest, France, which was even worse. But these strategic improvements were not merely strokes of luck contingent upon land conquest. They were parts of a long-laid and carefully executed plan running back many years.

Credit for them goes to Vice Admiral Karl Doenitz, who almost single-handed had built up the German U-boat fleet while the British and French obligingly looked the other way. It was Doenitz who had invented the system of knock-down submarines and had scattered factories all over Germany to produce them while the Treaty of Versailles was still in effect. It was he who had perfected the supersensitive hydrophone comparable to the Asdic; he who had developed a standard method of communication between submarine and scout plane. It was Doenitz who had replaced the stiff-necked decorum of the earlier U-boats with a camaraderie which made them "happy ships." And now that Hitler had handed him the bases, he was ready to sally forth into the Atlantic and torpedo the world.

ENGLAND'S TROUBLES INCREASE

According to unofficial British estimates the first year of antisubmarine measures had netted "a minimum of 250" German and Italian boats destroyed. But however well the Allies had done the new U-boats that came in crates more than made up for the loss. The tremendous toll of ships that had accompanied the evacuation at Dunkirk was repeated all summer by attacks on vessels in the open ocean—attacks from the new bases in western France.

Convoy had been considered the satisfactory answer to sub attack; it was so no longer. Swarms of U-boats lay in wait far out into the Atlantic, while overhead their companion planes ranged across the ocean to spot the Allied ships and radio back the speed and numbers of the convoys and the character of their naval escort. Focke-Wulf long-range bombers maintained a regular round-trip beat between France and Norway, swinging in a wide arc over some 1,500 miles of sea and cutting across every possible convoy route to Britain.

British shipping difficulties were at the same time

increasing enormously. Besides the basic load of 25,000 tons of foodstuffs *per day,* there was a new burden of lumber and iron, formerly obtained from Scandinavia but now to be hauled from Canada and the United States. The trickle of American fighter planes and munitions was steadily widening into a stream; these too required more and more ships. The available cargo fleet, robbed of any American support by the Neutrality Act, was rapidly becoming inadequate. British shipyards were building frenziedly, but the Luftwaffe had

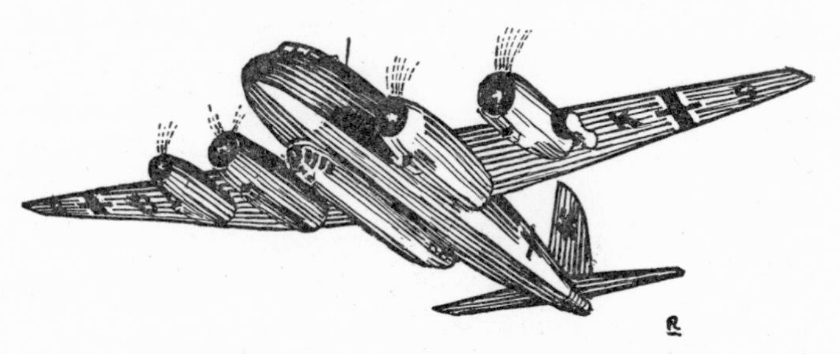

FIGURE 28. *Focke-Wulf Scouting Plane*

located many of them and was bombing them mercilessly.

The strain on naval escorts was increasing in the same ratio. British cruisers and destroyers were remaining on sea duty twenty-five to twenty-eight days out of every month—an impossible load on the endurance of both ships and crews. Their troubles were further aggravated by reports that the German cruiser *Deutschland* and other craft were loose on the high seas as surface raiders, thus forcing convoying all the way eastward from American shores. As summer turned into fall the full horror of aerial attack struck the Island Kingdom. Britain was facing a blacker moment than she had in 1917.

BRITISH AND AMERICAN ANSWERS

But the Englishmen kept their heads. While the people ashore took it without flinching; while the R.A.F. began to show Hitler that he had made his first real mistake, the Navy struck back at the U-boats with everything it could muster. A perpetual rain of bombs began to drop on the submarine bases in France and Norway, and long-range sallies were made against factories in Hamburg and the docks at Kiel. Boldly and suddenly the British made the surprise seizure of Iceland, both to prevent the Germans from doing the same thing and to obtain a base for harassing Nazi plane and submarine routes west from Norway. They then bent their convoy routes to the north to get away from the hornet's nest of U-boats in the vicinity of France. At the same time they sent a desperate plea for American help. President Roosevelt, ignoring powerful isolationist pressure, arranged the famous destroyer-naval base swap.

On September 5, 1940, a flotilla of eight "over-age" destroyers sailed from Boston with skeleton crews. On the 6th it reached Halifax, took on British complements, and went to sea on a practice cruise to familiarize the new owners with every detail of operation. On the 9th the little vessels were ready to start convoy work, their decks and magazines crammed with American depth charges and ammunition. Thereafter, week by week, more destroyers were retrieved from our de-

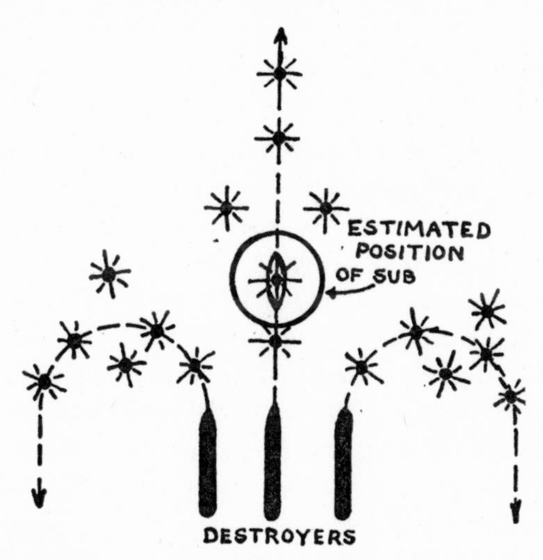

FIGURE 29. *Pattern of Depth Charges Laid over Submarine by Destroyers*

commissioned list and were sent into the Battle of the Atlantic, until finally fifty had been given. At the same time ten seagoing Coast Guard cutters were added. In return we got eight invaluable naval-base concessions reaching from Newfoundland to British Guiana.

Prime Minister Churchill has said that without this help the battle would have been lost. With it, the situation gradually mended. Through a terrible winter the British convoys drove their way eastward, steadily cutting a path through the U-boat concentrations. Losses were still huge, running close to 400,000 tons for each winter month; and although this represented a considerable drop from the peak of the previous summer it still neutralized Britain's ability to build and repair. March found the two opposing forces virtually in deadlock.

Since the beginning of unrestricted submarine warfare the spring months had invariably marked a sharp rise in sinkings. In 1941, they did so again. Losses shot up alarmingly, past the 400,000 mark, past 500,000, and on toward 600,000. Doenitz had decided on a smash toward victory, no matter what the cost in boats and men. Part of this he planned to achieve through the use of the battle cruisers *Scharnhorst* and *Gneisenau,* which he sent out to attack convoys at long range. They were immediately successful. Falling upon one convoy they sunk every ship in it, for a score of 100,000 tons. But the British had an antidote for that, and both warships were soon air-battered wrecks lying in the drydocks at Brest. Doenitz did not care; he favored submarine warfare in any case, and now he came forward with a surprise he had been saving for some time. This was the *Rudelsystem,* or wolf-pack method of attack. Instead of using his boats as solo performers he ordered them out in flotillas of two to a dozen, to harry their victims en masse.

THE WOLF PACK

DURING the first year of the war, the U-boats had operated as of old, largely in the daytime. This was necessary for accurate torpedoing by periscope. But a rapidly improving Asdic, aided by aerial scouting and better methods of laying depth charges, had made it suicidal for a sub to be caught near a convoy in the daylight hours. As a result the Germans had been forced to attack only at night. A handicap at first, this rapidly proved to be even deadlier to merchant-ship concentrations. The large cruiser submarines soon learned to lie in wait for a convoy on the surface in the dark, with long-range listening devices working on their conning towers. As the convoy approached, these surface raiders maneuvered into position at one side and loosed several torpedoes at once, fanning them out so as to take in as large a target as possible. Three direct hits out of a salvo of four were not uncommon. With the convoy in confusion, the U-boat would crash dive and get away, then race ahead at high surface speeds and lie in wait to attack again.

Night operation proving so promising, Doenitz determined to develop it to its ultimate efficiency by capitalizing on the panic he could cause in the dark. The use of pack hunting was the obvious means to do it. For this purpose he sent out large numbers of the small 500-ton U-boats, which were the easiest and quickest to assemble on the French coast. Groups of them, in charge of the ablest commander available, went out to lie in wait submerged. Rising to the surface at night they would receive radio instructions from the large cruiser subs to the west, then proceed to a rendezvous with the unlucky convoy.

The wolf-pack method made such an immediate ten-strike that it has been standard German practice ever since. There are several variations in use. One is for the pack to dive under the approaching convoy and come up in the midst of it, torpedoing in all directions at once. With explosions on every hand the escort vessels cannot tell whence the attack comes, and so frequently miss their quarry in the confusion. In this situation the Asdic is much hampered because its own vessels are in the way, and also because the subs, being on the surface, present less hull area for the reflection of sound. Pursuit, too, is defeated by crash diving with the help of automatically closing conning-tower hatches, and by the fact that the crowded condition of the area prevents satisfactory depth-charge operations.

An alternative pack method sends the submarine leader on ahead to single out and attack a ship in a far corner of the convoy. As soon as the escort is busy hunting down the marauder the companion U-boats pick out other vessels widely separated and torpedo them with ease, then slink away before they are discovered.

As the graph of losses shows, the wolf-pack method caused a serious rise in sinkings throughout the spring of 1941—so serious, in fact, that in June the British Admiralty stopped publishing losses altogether. Again strong pleas were made for American help, which resulted in the United States' coastal patrol being extended to Greenland, and soon after to the entire North Atlantic as far east as Iceland. The only hope for England lay in overwhelming the U-boats with numbers.

AMERICAN HELP AGAIN

THESE extended patrols did not mean that we had gone to war with Germany *diplomatically*. President Roosevelt had decided to beat the Nazis at their own psychological game. He therefore declared the whole North Atlantic as far as Iceland a "defense area" for the American continent. It fooled the Germans not at all, and if they had been less busy fighting England the move would undoubtedly have brought a declaration of war then and there. But Hitler for the moment forbore. And on our side the Navy searched for but did not sink (so it said) German submarines. In any case, it was of vast help to the British to have reconnaissance done for them by American ships.

Another important nonbelligerent aid from America was the "Catalina" flying boat, a long-range, overwater bomber delivered to England at that time in substantial numbers. These ships, based on Iceland and Northern Ireland, maintained a wide scouting sweep over the danger zone carrying bombs and depth charges and maintaining close radio contact with convoys and headquarters ashore. They made effective offense units also; their score of U-boats sunk, according to the best estimates, has run close to one-third of all submarines destroyed.

The importance of air attack, and particularly of air reconnaissance, upon submarine warfare was quickly appreciated. But as the U-boats worked stead-

FIGURE 30. *The Famous Catalina Flying Boat*

ily westward out of the range of land-based planes it became necessary to provide floating bases. Large convoys began taking aircraft carriers with them. When these were unavailable, commercial ships were hastily altered to serve in the same capacity. Every warship that was able to carry planes was fitted with a catapult, and some of the larger merchantmen received them as well. The true answer to the U-boat was gradually being worked out in the air.

THE SITUATION TEMPORARILY IMPROVED

BUT it was not the only answer. Another great advance was in the establishment ashore, "somewhere in England," of a command center and planning headquarters to gather and integrate up-to-the-minute information about convoys and their attackers. This place, buried deep in the ground in a coastal town, has since been organized into an aid almost as important as Asdic itself. On its walls a vast map of the Atlantic Ocean is spread before a crew of naval officers and WRENS (Women of the Naval Reserve), who move about on it colored markers representing every ship known to be at sea and white markers symbolizing the U-boats. The center is in constant communication by radio with the operating forces, both naval and air, and the positions of convoys are corrected at four-hour intervals. An admiral, the Commander of the Western Approaches, sits behind a glass screen, and from the visual data on the map, plans for the protection of the whole area and gives orders for individual forays in quest of the subs.

The sinkings for April, 1941, had topped 600,000 tons. With United States help and British organization they began to drop again. By June, they were down to 350,000, and still dropping. The short nights of the far North (three to four hours of darkness only), together with the United States Iceland Patrol started in July, gave a further reduction, so that the summer average for 1941 was estimated to be not in excess of 180,000 tons a month. In addition, an encouraging picture was given of the number of U-boats destroyed. On April 8 there were fifty officers and four hundred enlisted men of the German submarine service in a concentration camp in the west of England, indicating

FIGURE 31. *The Capture of a U-boat*

that fifty boats at least had been destroyed since the war began. (The method of computation is not clear; evidently the figure is derived from a combination of the boats surrendered and those known to have been sunk with all hands.) Also, the wolf pack was thought to give an exaggerated estimate of the number of submarines actually present; it was believed that there were not more than sixty U-boats in the Atlantic at any one time.

But, as before, there was a reverse side to the picture. Late summer found the sinkings again on the increase. Coincidently, reports from Germany insisted that the Nazis had so far outrun U-boat destruction as to have 300 in service, with fully 100 on active duty continually. Doenitz boasted that the total would soon reach 600. Hidden factories all over the Reich were turning them out day and night; it was even reported that many new U-boats were being towed up the Rhine, down the Rhone Canal and the Rhone River, and so to the Mediterranean, without running the aerial blockade of the sea approaches. A further story told of large numbers of midget subs, carrying only five men, which were to infest the shores of England.

Characteristic Hitlerian exaggeration notwithstanding, sinkings bore the reports out, and Britain once more had to call for outside help. The United States had just put the lease-lend program into effect, and we were asked to take on the job of getting the vast quantities of material delivered. The fiction of neutrality had long since been given up in all except political circles; naval vessels had even been reported as sinking a U-boat or two on the North Atlantic route. The incident of the *Greer* now brought the showdown.

AMERICA INTERVENES

ON SEPTEMBER 11, the President went on the air with his famous "Shoot-on-Sight" address, bringing to light our paradoxical position in an unneutral world.

"The Navy Department has reported to me that on the morning of September 4th the United States destroyer *Greer* (while carrying mail to Iceland) was attacked by a submarine. Germany admits that it was a German submarine. . . . In spite of what Hitler's propaganda bureau has invented . . . I tell you the blunt fact that the German submarine fired first upon this American destroyer without warning and with deliberate design to sink her. (She) was proceeding on a legitimate mission. . . . This was piracy—legally and morally. It was not the first nor the last act of piracy which the Nazi Government has committed against the American flag in this war. Attack has followed attack."

The President mentioned the sinking of the *Robin Moore* in the spring, and then disclosed that an American battleship had been followed by a German submarine in July, but had outmaneuvered it. Adding several other examples of unprovoked attack he ended with this ringing statement:

"From now on, if German or Italian vessels enter the waters, the protection of which is necessary for American defense, they do so at their own peril. . . . The orders which I have given . . . to the United States Army and Navy are to carry out that policy—at once."

That meant open warfare on the U-boats by a nation still technically at peace with the Reich. As in the summer of 1917, the crushing force of fresh warships, manned by fresh crews, began to be felt at once. By

FIGURE 32. *First American Ship Torpedoed in World War II*

November, the Admiralty could announce that it had captured 807 U-boat men; 100 subs sunk if the ratio still held. Patrol was so good now that the wolf pack found it impossible to make its strikes, even at night. Convoys were not running blacked out any more; the whole ocean around them was turned into noonday by searchlights and floods. Destroyers and corvettes rushed up and down between the lanes of ships, picking off the enemy the moment they appeared.

Easy pickings in the Western Approaches were over. The Battle of the Atlantic was "won."

However, the victory even now was only a stalemate. What it amounted to was that British and American shipbuilding could now equal, and perhaps slightly surpass, the rate at which vessels could be sunk in spite of the British and American antisubmarine campaign. At the same time the total of U-boats could be held down to little if any increase.

For this situation the Germans had still another answer: They could move westward and open up a new hunting ground off America herself. Alone, this might not have been difficult to meet. But in December the Japanese obligingly threw in the waters of the Pacific. In one hour's bombing at Pearl Harbor the 64,000,000 square miles of the Pacific Ocean were added to the naval "front." A fresh and infinitely more deadly phase of the conflict had begun.

CHAPTER TEN

THE BATTLE OF AMERICA

AT THE moment of Pearl Harbor the United States and Britain were in a desperate situation. It was imperative that the Battle of the Atlantic stay "won," so that the vast stream of lease-lend goods might continue to flow to England and Russia. Yet both Allies suddenly and desperately needed escort vessels elsewhere: the British to bolster campaigns in the East; we to start materiel flowing to Australia. Our own Navy awoke, on December 7, with a two-ocean war on its decks and a one-and-a-quarter-ocean force to fight it with. The Atlantic Fleet had always been kept at a minimum; now, because of the ships sacrificed to gross negligence at Hawaii, it had to be robbed of every last cruiser and destroyer that could be spared for Pacific convoy service. Obviously no deletions could be made from the eastern Atlantic, so they came out of coastal patrol.

Into this perfect opening Vice Admiral Doenitz began to pour his U-boats without delay. It was the old game of taking candy from a child, which the Germans adored. The tremendous show of bravery in setting fire to unarmed tankers and burning their crews to death was the true expression of Aryan superiority. There was doubtless much rejoicing in Emden and

Wilhelmshaven when orders came to move west to the American coast. The hunting had not been too good of late in the chilly waters north of Great Britain. The Caribbean and the Gulf Stream looked like heaven to the U-boat crews.

MAKINGS OF THE PRESENT SITUATION

As THE Nazis sized things up their Christmas present from the Japs looked good. The United States and Canada had a combined Atlantic coast line of some 5,000 miles, not including the innumerable bays and inlets. The whole length of it was dotted with important harbors and estuaries jammed with war shipping. Every mile of it offered good hunting, for it was all in use as a vital highway for the Arsenal of Democracy. The Navy did not come within shouting distance of having adequate patrol protection. In fact, it was likely that thorough protection would prove to be impossible over so vast a stretch of ocean. The only American answer, as the Nazis saw it, was the use of convoy in all coastal waters, and this they knew was out of the question for a long time to come. Alone and unarmed, the hundreds of merchantmen would be so many clay pigeons for German torpedoes.

It was likewise encouraging to remember that a large number of coastwise vessels were tankers serving the vital industries of the East. Alert Nazi diplomats had already attended a dress rehearsal of a petroleum shortage and had transmitted to Berlin extravagant estimates of the havoc to the war program that tanker sinkings would cause. Better yet, there was the peculiar arrangement of refineries on the Dutch islands off Venezuela. A successful throttling of these would dry up three quarters of all the high-octane gasoline used on the European fronts.

Another shipping plum would be the steady line of cargo boats bringing bauxite ore from Dutch Guiana to Gulf ports. Bauxite was the principal source of aluminum, without which planes could not fly. Then there was the Panama Canal. If it could be blockaded or made impassable by surrounding mine fields, the Pacific effort would be badly slowed. And finally, that delightful Pan-American solidarity on which the United States had spent years and millions could be badly upset by U-boats lurking off the West Indies. Altogether, the prospects were alluring. There did not seem to be much that the United States could do about it.

The combination of mine barrage, convoy, and patrol had beaten the submarine in British waters in World War I. But for the United States to mine its own waters effectively would be close to impossible. There were no constricted passages except the Florida Strait and the St. Lawrence entrances, and these were deep channels swept by violent currents and impractical to mine. At best only the principal harbors could be protected. But the U-boats did not want to enter these anyway.

In addition to all this, German strategy counted on a violent wave of American protest as soon as sinkings started. United States citizens would be frightened; they were not like the English, calm and grim. Their isolationists would seize upon this new excuse to howl the Navy home to maintain the traditional sanctity of American shores. The Nazis did not believe Washington would fall for this, but they anticipated enough dissention and confusion to place an ugly burden on war production.

Some of this was wishful thinking, for there were alternatives to carrying oil by sea, and the American spirit turned out better than the Germans had hoped. But the main strike for the U-boats would be, not against coastwise commerce, but against *ships*. World shipping was like a vast balloon; a hole in it anywhere would be equally serious in draining the supply of lifting gas. The German position seemed like a "natural." Compulsory theaters of war were being forced on the United Nations all over the world, every one of them hand-picked by the enemy because of Allied stupidity and unpreparedness. While Axis victory on any single front would be extremely serious, clean-cut Allied victories would have to be obtained on all fronts before the democracies could terminate the war.

SUBMARINE WARFARE COMES TO AMERICA

THIS analysis, frankly from the German point of view, shows how complicated was the problem which confronted our strategists when the U-boat onslaught began in December, 1941. It partly explains why sinkings were not immediately stopped when it was evident that a definite submarine campaign, rather than a hit-and-run raid, was on. It indicates that control of the coastal U-boat was a job we were not able to do along with everything else. The remainder of the explanation is a matter of internal politics and bungling. In so far as these things have prevented the control of the submarine menace, we ourselves, not the U-boat, are to blame. At the beginning we seem to have hoped that the serious coastal situation would take care of itself. When it did not, measures were reluctantly taken, not in the all-out manner which would have made them effective, but with certain reservations which prevented first-rate results. What we suffer now in the heavy and still increasing toll of ships is the result of our own choice.

It is never possible to say exactly how many ships have been sunk, but in a typical period in mid-1942 the number varied from five to ten a week in the American theater alone. This, with the losses on all other fronts, quickly brought the totals back to the alarming proportions of early 1941. Exuberantly, the Germans claimed a million tons of tankers destroyed between January 14 and March 24. That meant 200 to 500 ships, and was no doubt an exaggeration. But on May 20 the Office of Price Administration said that 150 vessels had gone down in American waters since the start of the war. By July 10, the number of victims officially admitted by the Navy had risen to 337. Whatever the true figures, we then were and still are in the midst of a desperate struggle with the U-boat, and the outcome is not yet clear.

What, then, is the size and character of the U-boat fleet which has caused these depredations? Again an average must be struck between Nazi claims and the sketchy computations made from restricted official figures. The best estimate at the time of the Pearl Harbor attack put the German total at 225 boats in service and probably an equal number building or planned. Years of U-boat warfare have shown that about a third of the submarine fleet is actively at work on the hunting grounds at any one time; another third is en route; while the remainder is laid up for repairs and resting the crews. That would suggest that about seventy-five Nazi craft were available for all stations when the United States entered the war. Assuming a third of these to have been kept in British waters to force the maintenance of Atlantic convoy, about fifty may be counted on to have opened the Battle of America—that is, fifty on the ground at a time, with another fifty en route across the ocean. And this second fifty, of course, would be able to knock off whatever stray merchantmen they encountered.

In mid-May, American diplomats and newspapermen returning from internment in Germany revealed Hitler's boast that 180 to 300 submarines were busy in the Atlantic, a figure that checks well enough with Allied guesses to indicate that the Führer may not have lied. Let us say that he does have over a hundred subs in battle trim in Atlantic waters all the time.

Anywhere from sixty to eighty of them may be continually within sight of the United States. That is enough submarines to sink every vessel that comes along unprotected.

In the spring of 1942 the Nazis claimed a submarine building rate of twenty-five per month—three hundred a year, and actual commissioning of eighteen per month. Whether this inflow of new boats is raising the total arrayed against us is again a matter of guesswork, but it probably is raising it at least somewhat. Even the President does not know what the rate of U-boat destruction is. Every sort of ruse is used by the sub commanders to make the Navy think that depth charges have struck home, when in actual fact the supposed victims have made good their escape. On top of this, sinkings that are beyond question are kept secret. It is considered one of the best weapons against U-boat morale never to know exactly what was the fate of comrades who do not come home.

Concerning this secrecy the Navy has this to say:

"Some of the recent visitors to our territorial waters will never enjoy the return portion of their voyage. . . . But there will be no information given out about the fate of the enemy submarine excursionists who don't get home, until that information is no longer of aid and comfort to the enemy. . . . The Nazis think themselves pretty clever in the field of psychological warfare. Secrecy surrounding the fate of their submarines is a counter-blow the American people can give them which may serve to shake some of their superconfidence."

This slightly flip rejoinder is open to question on the grounds that American submarine men also are in the dark about the fate of their comrades, yet the fact does not seem to destroy their spirit or their eagerness to ship against the enemy. At the same time, the suppression of figures of American success against the U-boat tends to destroy American confidence in our own Navy—an item quite as valuable to the Nazis as the mystery is supposed to be to us. Thus the morale of the people of the United States is set against the morale of the German submarine crew. Who can say which one needs the greater support?

As to the type and tonnage of the attackers, a little more can be said. Most of them are not large, being of the compact 500-ton class, which is smaller than the O-boats we use for training and which we consider to be obsolescent. They carry crews of fifty men and a load of about a dozen torpedoes. In addition they are strongly armed with a deck gun and machine guns. Their cruising radius is better than 10,000 miles. But lest we get too confident that we know our enemy's strength, an Associated Press dispatch from London in late May says that "the Germans have developed 3,000-ton submarines carrying two 8-inch guns and 14 torpedoes, for long-range raiding and are believed to be sending them in relays to harry the eastern coast. . . ." If the report is true it indicates that the Nazis intend to make the Battle of America a major engagement.

Still more alarming are recent discoveries made by the Navy from an examination of a captured U-boat. These submarine hulls are capable of submerging to

600 feet—twice the standard limit—and are thus able to reach levels for which present depth charges are not designed. Worse, the new raiders operate under water without batteries. Their engines are of a novel design which can run submerged on oxygen and hydrogen supplied from bottles without depleting the sub's air supply. If any considerable number of U-boats have such engines it is indeed serious, for the very large spaces required for batteries will have been replaced by extra torpedoes and fuel, and their staying power in American waters will have been greatly increased.

A 10,000-mile radius for boats based on the coast of France would leave about 3,000 miles clear for dallying along our shores—two or three weeks of fighting time. But it is not certain that all Nazi subs make this round trip regularly. There are many reports that U-boats refuel in our own waters, either from large mother submarines or surface supply ships, or from hidden island bases. Officially the Navy denies the presence of enemy land bases, but there may still be some in the thousands of hidden coves and inlets, particularly in tropical waters. A Japanese base of this kind was found and destroyed in Lower California early in the war.

That traitorous Americans are ferrying oil out to the U-boats is unlikely; it would be exceedingly difficult under the eyes of the harbor patrols. But there is the near certainty that oil is obtained from captured tankers and by contact with secret expeditions sent out by fifth columnists on both sides of the Atlantic.

Moreover, there is proof that submarines have been

making contact with our shores for the purpose of gaining information on ship sailings and cargoes. After a recent sinking in Florida waters the survivors brought in the story that a kind-hearted German had tossed them a loaf of fresh bread in the wrapper of a Miami baking concern. There have also been accounts of German rubber boats found in secluded coves. It is admitted that such landings have been made in England, and their use here has lately been confirmed by the capture of eight spies known to have landed from U-boats. Survivors of sunken ships have reported that U-boat commanders knew accurate details of the vessel's burdens and destinations. There is reason to believe that fifth-column activity plays a part, and probably an important one, in the submarine war.

The first U-boat attack in the Battle of America was upon the *Norness,* only twenty miles off the Long Island shore in December. The survivors said they were machine-gunned in their boats. That was the keynote of the new campaign, soon to be made the more horrible by death by fire as tankers filled with oil kindled from the torpedo explosions. The rate of crew survival has sometimes dropped to 30 per cent in this coastal war, as compared with 70 per cent in eastern Atlantic waters. It is evident that the hope of the Nazis has been to frighten merchant crews into staying ashore. To this end they are reported to be using incendiary torpedoes.

At the present writing the situation is deadly serious. Sinkings are still definitely on the increase; the shipbuilding program, though splendid on paper, is not yet stopping the gap. The Maritime Commission admitted that in April only thirty-six new vessels went into service. The record is steadily improving, but is still far from good enough. U-boats are still being turned out faster than they can be destroyed, so that there is a steady net increase in enemy forces. And they are getting steadily bolder. Depredations in the St. Lawrence and at the mouth of the Mississippi are successful—in areas actually surrounded by American territory. Traffic in the Gulf of Mexico has virtually stopped.

Eventually we can outbuild the German sinking rate and make it unimportant. But will "eventually" be soon enough? Shall we be forced into a Battle *For* the Atlantic first?

WHAT ARE WE DOING ABOUT IT?

THE war that came to the United States during the week of December 7, 1941, found us fast asleep in bed. Not at Pearl Harbor alone but especially along the Atlantic Coast. We were definitely not prepared for a submarine battle in home waters. From Maine to Florida the coast was undefended, except by the few ships and planes of the Coast Guard. Everything available was assigned to duty out toward Iceland, or was making ready for a dash to the Pacific. It was therefore necessary to build up a new coastal defense from scratch. That meant hundreds, even thousands, of small fast boats to carry out the proven antisubmarine measures. There were few on hand; for some reason naval planners had omitted them in all the building programs. Nor were there many yachts available for patrol duty, as in 1917. They had been offered but sidetracked on the excuse of inadequacy. The objection was only partially valid; the real trouble was that massive concentrations of bureaucrats blocked swift and determined action. Defense, it was insisted, must be standardized, blueprinted, unified, organized—and that would take time. Only in late May did Vice Admiral Adolphus Andrews, promoted from the command under which the *Normandie* was lost, finally admit that the Navy might accept private yachts and fishing vessels as auxiliaries. By that time the U-boat campaign had become a virtual stampede.

In the air the defense situation was just as unfavorable. The Army claimed jurisdiction over all coastal patrol, but had no experience in operating over water. The Navy, with a small number of seaplanes and a very few blimps, was relegated to offshore work exclusively. Authority was being jockeyed between the two. Everyone tried hard—most of all the courageous young pilots who flew the planes under confusing orders—but effectiveness was sacrificed to formality. In the two or three months while this situation was at its worst the Germans virtually denied us the use of our own waters.

Slowly the situation began to right itself. The loss of the *Normandie* through gross negligence at her New York pier so aroused the country that unification of command had to be achieved in all naval matters.

Since that time things have been going better. But they are still not going well enough; and the reason is that the enormous disadvantage of having been caught unprepared has not yet been made up. It would be pleasant to be able to assign failure to simple mechanical causes beyond human control; unfortunately, this cannot be done for the Battle of America. Nothing is

FIGURE 33. *U. S. Antisubmarine Net Layer*

gained by denying that the failure has been one of persons and that improvement has come largely from public pressure. Hitler set out to make this a psychological war. He has been able to capitalize on psychological incompetence everywhere.

Adequate defense of coastwise shipping was at first impossible to the Navy because convoy was out of the question. Worse, there was a definite lack of co-operation between civilian vessels and the naval high command. Years of unrestrained union activity at sea had established a deplorable lack of discipline. It was not possible to give merchant captains and crews rigid orders and force them to obey. Many ships were lost through deliberate disobedience to regulations which would have prevented them from running afoul of the U-boats. Eventually all this was somewhat corrected in the unification of authority under the Maritime Commission.

On the brighter side the Navy was steadily cleaning house. All coastal defense was finally gathered under clear naval authority and specific plans laid out for attacking the submarine. Anti-U-boat strategy was divided into defensive and offensive measures, and both received full co-operation up to the limit of the means available.

On the defensive side merchant ships are now being armed at top speed, and hundreds of gun crews are being trained and put aboard them. At the same time new merchant-marine officers are going to Navy schools to learn the latest in antisubmarine practice. On top of this the Navy is putting on pressure to induct civilian crews into the service, so that laxity of discipline can be corrected. This last is still considerably in the future.

Air patrols are maintained along all shipping lanes, and though spread thin they succeed in warning ships of the approach of subs in time to save them. These patrols also help crew morale by frequently spotting lifeboats and saving many lives.

Something has been done to improve the routing of ships. Vessels are ordered as far inshore as possible, and are sometimes told to lay over in port every night. But the use of the inland waterway north from Florida is mostly wishful thinking. It is too small and shallow for anything but barges, of which there are too few to do much good. For a time help was given by the railroads

FIGURE 34. *Sky Glow Silhouettes Ships and Makes Them Easy Victims of U-boats*

in shortening the routes of northbound vessels by transshipping their cargoes in Gulf ports; but the Nazis soon tightened their U-boat ring and stopped it. There are no safe waters for American shipping to ply. The only nonmilitary measure that promises help today is the "dimout" imposed by the Army on all coastal towns, so that ships shall not stand out as perfect targets against the night-sky glow.

On the offensive side the Navy has put into service considerable numbers of "PT-boats" and other high-speed, motor-driven craft for reconnaissance and attack. These vessels, about seventy feet long, are built along the lines of racing motorboats, with as many as three gasoline engines driving three screws, and are capable of forty to sixty knots. They are fitted with four torpedo tubes, machine guns, and depth charges,

FIGURE 35. *Fast Torpedo Boat for Antisubmarine Patrol*

and are so light in draft that they cannot be attacked by a submarine unless it is on the surface, where it is hopelessly inferior in speed and maneuverability. The PT's are commanded by one officer and carry from six to ten men. They can be built in a month out of plywood or thin sheet steel. Large numbers are planned.

Older types of patrol craft are also being turned out in quantity: the famous 110-foot subchasers of the last war, also various smaller and larger vessels that are sturdy enough to carry guns and depth charges. The only principle which can be relied on to beat the submarine is to overwhelm it with so many enemies of all types that it can find no free area in which to work.

Experience in the Battle of the Atlantic has shown that much of the surface duty can be better performed in the air, where the range is enormously increased and the offensive power is almost as good. The airplane has the advantage that it can detect a submerged sub if it is not more than fifty feet down in clear water. It can also spot the periscope "feather" several miles away. Once discovered in the daytime the U-boat has a poor chance of getting away before the plane is over it unloading bombs. Radio communication with headquarters ashore, similar to the control center in England, is giving the Navy a steadily improving knowledge of the position of all subs. In reconnaissance work a new branch of civilian flyers is turning in a fine performance, volunteering for several hours a week of offshore duty in nonmilitary planes.

But the latest and most important innovation is the use of the nonrigid airship, or blimp, which is already proving itself nearly the equal of naval escort in convoy work. The great advantage of the balloon type of aircraft is that it combines a top speed of some eighty miles an hour with the ability to stop dead in the air and hover while dropping its bombs. It can even use a listening device and follow a submarine after it has submerged. The present blimp is a helium-filled bag holding up to 600,000 cubic feet, about 250 feet long and 70 feet high. It has twin engines and a cruising radius of 1,500 miles. It is operated by two officers and a very small crew, whose duties are among the most ex-

FIGURE 36. *Shadow of Submerged Submarine, Seen from the Air*

hausting in the Navy, since the management of the large gas bags in winds and vertical currents requires exceptional skill. But the effectiveness of the new method is proving so great that the present number is

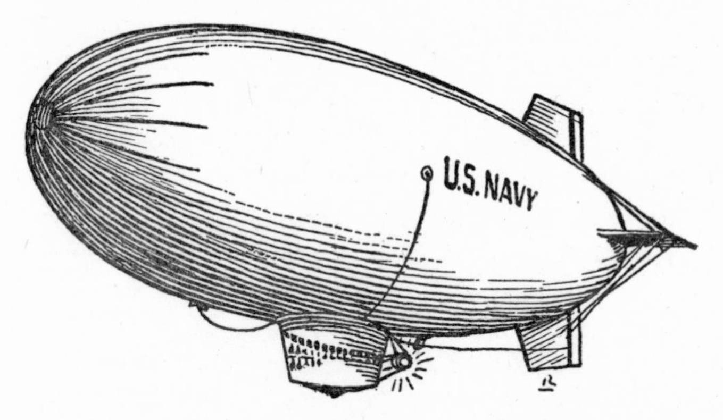

FIGURE 37. *Blimp on Patrol in American Waters*

to be increased to seventy-two, and larger sizes are being planned. The demand of the lighter-than-air program for thousands of square feet of rubberized fabric is a contributing cause for the rubber shortage today.

RESULTS SO FAR

AS ON the industrial front, the progress of antisubmarine measures was painfully slow at first, but is gradually moving toward crushing strength. Numbers will win, and it is numbers that we are striving for: 18,000,000 tons of ships; tens of thousands of planes and blimps; hundreds of thousands of depth charges and bombs. There is even talk of sending precious freight by air, and no doubt if the war lasts long enough this will be done.

There are several significant facts which indicate that the U-boat is not the undisputed master of the western Atlantic that Hitler intended it to be. One is that the Panama Canal has not been attacked. Successful closing of this waterway would have been a crushing blow to the Navy, yet the German subs have got no nearer to it than the island of Aruba, 700 miles away; and even that vital point has not been seriously harmed. The reason is that the oil ships bringing the crude oil from the mainland have received full convoy protection. Nor has the constant stream of bauxite vessels been interrupted, nor yet the huge convoys of soldiers and supplies moving east and south from New York. These, too, have received the complete protection of naval escort.

Merchant ships are still running along the coast. There is as yet no difficulty in signing on crews for the new vessels as they come along; and the survivors of the torpedoings are going back for more, to a man. The principal emotion that fires these castaways of the war is rage and the desire to get back "for another crack at the guy that thinks he can run me off the sea."

That all is not serene in the submarine world is shown by the report that German insurance companies now compute the life expectancy of a submarine man to be only fifty days. Further evidence of trouble is given in the complaint of a U-boat commander who angrily went on the air in Berlin.

"When we approached the enemy to give him his death blow, we were greeted by a hail of gunfire. Heavy guns and machine guns which had been hidden by artificial sides and other objects of the cargo boat

FIGURE 38. *Depth Charges on the Stern of a Patrol Boat*

suddenly came into action. Depth charges were hurled at us. So clever had been the maneuvering that we were caught unawares and our command bridge was hit by shrapnel.

I was furious when I realized that this trap might have cost us another U-boat. For only by a miracle were we able to crash-dive and escape from the heavy fire without losing our boat."

The unsporting Americans, it seems, have added the Q-boat to their hunt for the rats of the sea.

CHAPTER ELEVEN

AMERICAN SUBS IN ACTION

WHEN the airplane has finally forced the great navies of the world to seek shelter in museums, history will undoubtedly record that the submarine was the last to go. Of all types of warship the undersea boat is least vulnerable to aerial attack. The invisibility which earned it a first grudging approval eighty years ago remains as its only real defense against the weapon of the future.

Thus, when great naval battles are absurdities to be avoided at all costs, the submarine will still go out to harass the enemy's trade and block the movement of troops. In the Pacific war of today we are having a preview of this very condition. Already there is work for the fleets far more important than meeting and annihilating each other: convoy. Neither side has an easy job in overcoming the vast distances of the Far East. Much has been written of the interminable journeys our men and equipment must make to reach the battleground. But Japan has a similar problem. She had to traverse nearly 1,400 miles of open ocean to land her troops on the beaches of Luzon; Java was 2,600 miles away; the Aleutians, 2,600. These long hauls were just as vulnerable to submarine attack as the worst stretches of the eastern Atlantic or the coastal waters of the United States. Her convoy problem has been as difficult as ours.

The objective of both sides has been to prevent the enemy from moving his land forces by sea, while successfully moving his own. In the old days naval concentrations would have carried this out alone. But with modern warplanes in the sky they can do so no longer. In an area where the enemy has clear air superiority, surface operations are plain suicide. Japan has had such superiority consistently, so that action against her has had to be made by planes and submarines.

As a result our submarine force has already chalked up a distinguished record in the Pacific, being responsible for fully one-third of all enemy vessels destroyed. In the first four months it accounted for forty-two Japanese ships sunk, with twelve more probably sunk and eleven damaged. Thirteen of these were cruisers and destroyers, and several were aircraft carriers and transports. Our submarine score against Nippon is several times as high as hers is against us.

HOW THE SUBMARINE FORCES LINE UP

At the start of hostilities the United States had from 120 to 140 subs in commission with 70-odd building. A large proportion of these were in the Pacific. The majority of them are of the large cruiser classes between 1,000 and 1,500 tons, with a range of 10,000 miles or better on one loading of fuel.

Set against this fleet, the Japanese (unless they have hoodwinked the world in this respect also) have a total of no more than eighty boats. With their usual foresight they built these very large, mostly capable of cruising 15,000 miles or more and hence well able to attack our coast from their home bases. Among the number are several of the I-16 class of over 2,000 tons, carrying five-inch guns and making in excess of twenty knots on the surface. In addition, a few are 2,700-ton giants fitted as mine layers, able to sow sixty mines per trip in our waters. Nearly all these boats are faithful copies of successful German types, and all carry at least six torpedo tubes. One, aping the French *Surcouf,* carries a small scouting plane.

EARLY ATTACKS OF JAP SUBS

JAPAN started out with what she hoped would be a spectacular innovation: the two-man miniature, or suicide submarine. Launched either from an airplane carrier of some other mother ship, these tiny weapons were expected to penetrate Pearl Harbor and blow up whatever the air-raiders missed. The plan did not come off, presumably because the crews were not expert enough. Only two reached Hawaii, and both were captured. One got into the harbor mouth and fouled the protective nets. The other was driven ashore on an outlying beach.

These little subs were curiously reminiscent of the early Lake and Holland boats. They were forty-one feet long and five feet in diameter, of the single hull variety. Inside they were remarkably complete. They carried two torpedoes in tubes forward, and had a

FIGURE 39. *The* Surcouf

simple electric-motor drive fed by the usual storage batteries. An officer sat amidships in a miniature control room with a periscope to his eye and all the usual operating instruments within reach, including a gyrocompass and the latest torpedo-aiming and firing devices. A small conning tower with an entrance hatch rose four feet above him. In the after compartment huddled the crew of one man, in telephonic communication with the skipper. Besides the motor controls he had a radio receiver and an underwater hydrophone set. The only novel feature was a 300-pound charge of TNT packed away in the stern for destroying the boat in case it was about to be captured. Neither of the Jap commanders obeyed orders and used it.

The two-man subs failed through ineffective handling. Their occasional use since only confirms their poor reputation.

After the shock of Pearl Harbor people on our West Coast expected a ruthless attack by submarines on the

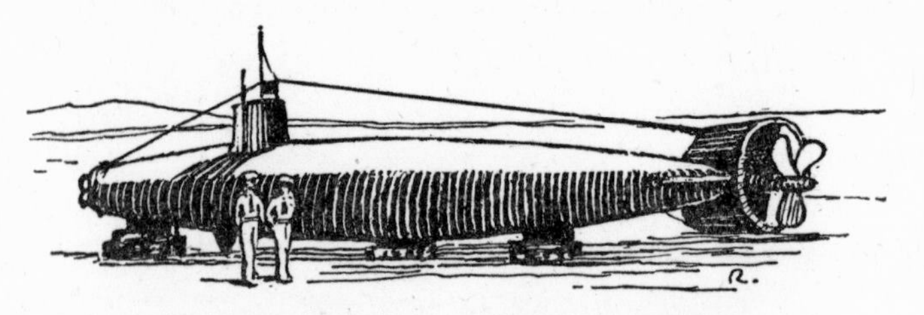

FIGURE 40. *Two-man Japanese Submarine*

German plan. The Japanese tried to oblige, but failed dismally. Their boats are first-rate but their crews are definitely inferior. A week before Christmas, 1941, several subs arrived to prey upon coastwise shipping. Of nine merchantmen attacked, only one was sunk and two were damaged. An equally clumsy attempt was made to shell an oil field near Santa Barbara in February, and resulted only in demolishing a sheet-iron pump house. Twenty-five misses were scored at a range of half a mile. In all the attacks marksmanship like this was the cause of failure.

The Japs were not lacking in nerve. One boat rigged herself out with a false superstructure (the origin of which was probably a friendly fishing boat from the mainland) and tried to decoy steamers into point-blank range. Other subs came so close inshore that thousands lined the beaches to watch them at work. But they caused little trouble. Most of the attacked ships got away by quick maneuvering, and planes soon drove the marauders off.

Either the Jap commanders had been misinformed as to the panic they would cause, or they were guilty of exceedingly poor judgment, for they repeatedly moved close to the shore in full daylight. A telephone lineman working on a pole near the coast looked out to sea one day and saw a submarine moving along on the surface. Quickly he snapped his portable phone onto a circuit and got through to an Army base near-by. While he was still up the pole he saw planes roar out to sea and destroy the sub before his eyes.

The object of these early Japanese visits was evidently to frighten the citizens and upset production in the near-by plane plants. This too was a failure. Air patrol promptly applied was the answer. And a valuable result was that several thousand potential foreign troublemakers were removed inland out of reach of fifth-column temptation. Since the early days of the war little has been heard of the long-range marauder from Japan, except for a sporadic shelling attack on the Oregon coast in June, in which a little grass was damaged. That there is still a threat, however, is proved by the dearth of tankers plying north to Oregon and Washington.

Nippon's submarines have not been successful even in their own home waters. They have been seen everywhere, but they rarely attack effectively. There is every evidence that their crews are technically inadequate to the grueling task of fighting a modern war. Recently two of them were caught and sunk by single

American bombing planes. In both cases the Japs were lying on the surface charging their batteries and did not awaken to the danger in time. One sub made such a precipitous crash dive that part of her crew was washed overboard and drowned. Depth charges sent the rest after them.

BATTLE OF THE EAST INDIES

Ineffective as one branch of the Japanese war machine may be, it is more than compensated for by the remainder. There is no better example of its enormous power and skill and its blind courage than the battle which culminated in the capture of Java and the attack upon Australia. And it is the only battle so far in which American submarines have definitely collaborated with units of the fleet.

Preliminary action began suddenly in the Straits of Macassar late in January. A huge Japanese invasion fleet headed south through the Straits was caught totally by surprise one night by a small force of American destroyers. Leading these in the attack, an American submarine came to the surface squarely between two Jap destroyers and sank them simultaneously "without warning." Before the convoy had time to scatter, American surface craft closed in and sank three transports and quickly retired. They were replaced immediately by cruisers and more submarines, and five more transports were downed. One of these subs was the *Sailfish,* once the ill-fated *Squalus,* which quickly justified the long months of salvage she had required by torpedoing an aircraft carrier and a cruiser.

For three days and nights the action raged almost continuously, with Dutch forces joining our own in a hit-and-run game. The Japs were forced to rush in heavy cruiser support, and several of these vessels, too, were lost. When the battle was over the score stood at about fifty Japanese warships and transports sunk. Not a single American vessel had been lost (if Washington has released all the facts). But in spite of the huge toll in ships and men the enemy pushed on, making successful landings in Borneo and Celebes. On February 4, they were raiding Java from the air. Three weeks later they had consolidated their positions and had invaded the island at both ends.

The battle for Java itself was unlike any military action in history. It was a tangled chaos of combats on land and sea and in air which raged continuously for seven days. The naval portion of it was a conglomeration of task-force fights and convoy attacks, complicated by incessant air bombardment by both sides. The affair developed so rapidly that the conventional pattern of approach, maneuver and strike, went by the board. Engagements developed on the instant, as the Navy repeatedly snatched the initiative from the enemy; there were a dozen separate battles going on at once.

American and Dutch units fought brilliantly, but they did not have a chance under a hostile umbrella of bombers. Early in the action the supply of Allied fighter planes gave out, rendering their own bombers so helpless that they had to be grounded and abandoned. With overwhelming air superiority the Japs then blasted the naval forces to bits without hindrance. Our submarines played a valiant part, making utmost use of their ability to hide from air attack, and accounted for many enemy transports and warships as well. The score has not been made public, but Admiral Thomas C. Hart, who commanded our forces at the time, stated on his return to America that submarines were the most effective vessels in the Asiatic Fleet. Subs alone of all our ships came out of the Java conflict without a loss (again if official releases are candid).

INDIVIDUAL SUBMARINE EXPLOITS

SINCE the morning of Pearl Harbor, American submarines in the Pacific have been quietly carrying out the individual forays for which they were so well designed. They have harassed the enemy and sunk his warships and his transports; they have gone on long and dangerous reconnaissance cruises and have slipped into besieged ports to bring help to beleaguered men. These are lonely and hazardous duties which have tested our undersea branch to the utmost and have found it adequate. Based either on Hawaii or Australia the subs have been forced to operate solo, traveling tens of thousands of miles and remaining absent regularly for weeks or months at a time.

In spite of the spectacular raids upon Japanese positions and the brilliant blows we have struck from time to time, it is still a fact that the first six months of war did not seriously impair enemy strength. At the start Japan had 5,600,000 tons of merchant vessels, and claimed to have seized 200 Allied ships in Nipponese ports—nearly a million tons more. We have sunk no more than 10 per cent of this—too little to prevent a consistent series of land seizures of utmost value to the enemy. The real achievement of our Navy has been glorious but negative; it has managed to keep 6,000 miles of sea lanes open for the westward movement of men and supplies. It has played a defensive role.

Like Germany, our only sustained naval offensive has been the submarine campaign against shipping. With an enormous handicap of distance, we are still trying to make that as effective a strangulation as the U-boats have done in the Atlantic.

The difficulties of submarine work have been multiplied by the high temperatures of the tropical seas and the coral-lined shoals on which no sub can safely lie. In spite of them, many magnificent exploits have been scored. Very early in the game the Japanese radio screamed that American submarines had "encircled" the islands. The truth was that no more than two or three boats had reached the vicinity of Japanese industrial ports, torpedoing everything that came along. Theirs was the success that the Japs had missed off California.

A typical exploit was that of the *Seawolf,* which carried on a lonely hunt in Java waters after the main battle was over. The operation was extremely dangerous because she was forced to run continuously, being denied a rest by the treacherous character of the bottom. Yet this submarine was able to dispose of a Japanese light cruiser, a destroyer, and a large transport; and to seriously damage two other cruisers, a transport, and various smaller vessels. Only the high skill of the *Seawolf's* men kept her from being lost.

Another sub's mission in the Java Sea was to prevent enemy warships from circling around to the south of the island, and thereby cutting off Allied escape from Tjilatjap. This boat stationed herself in the Lombok Strait and had the good fortune to discover a Japanese plane carrier silhouetted against the moonlight. Her own position was grave, for a previous attack on a destroyer flotilla had brought on pursuit, and she was being depth-charged and bombed at the time. In spite of this the sub commander steadied his periscope and released torpedoes which reduced the carrier to a wreck. Then he got safely away.

Still another adventure took place in the open ocean when one of our boats, on a submerged run, heard a ship above her and, on investigation, found it to be an enemy submarine. The Jap heard the American coming, and presently both ships were squared off for torpedo attack. But our "tin fish" leaped from its tube first, and the Japanese sub went down with all hands.

Among the most picturesque submarine exploits have been the daring relief expeditions to bring assistance to besieged Corregidor. While two out of every three Allied surface vessels were caught and sunk on their way into Manila Bay, the submarines always got through. One of these was the *Trout,* which slipped through the Japanese blockade early in February and docked at the island fortress in the night. She brought a desperately needed cargo of antiaircraft ammunition and a tremendous amount of encouragement. A similar exploit had been carried out by another sub before this, running supplies into Manila Bay and then remaining for a week to take on a fortune in gold from the Manila banks. During the sub's whole visit Japanese bombers were continuously busy overhead, but they did not discover her presence. All day and until midnight she lay dead on the bottom, then surfaced hastily and came into dock at Corregidor to load. And though the sub was finally detected by the enemy, she waited for a final shipment of state papers and bonds before making her escape.

In spite of their repeated dangerous missions American submarines have been remarkably untouched. Only four were reported lost in the first six months. Three of them, the *Perch,* the *Shark,* and the *S-56* simply disappeared, and their fate is unknown. The *Sealion,* lying at Cavite Naval Base when the Japs struck, had to be destroyed to keep her out of enemy hands.

Submarine men in the Pacific are probably under the greatest strain of any naval personnel. One of their most valuable services is to seek out enemy concentrations and size up their strength. The radio reports they then send back to headquarters often give their positions away, and they must run for their lives.

Nevertheless, the sub crews do not complain. Like the rest of the front-line Navy they are willing to die for the sake of avenging themselves for Pearl Harbor. Even under the extreme conditions of submerged warfare the undersea man prefers his duty to any other. As Captain Robinson of the cruiser *Marblehead* put it, he has the courage, the stamina, and the resourcefulness to make a success of the most difficult technique in the maritime world.

THE SUMMING UP

THIS is the story of submarine warfare up to the present, told in all the detail that is available. Obviously it is incomplete, punctuated by gaps that will not be filled in till the war is long past. The submarine weapon has totally changed modern naval strategy, and it will remain in a controlling position until the airplane has driven it to a watery grave in some future struggle.

Optimistic reports notwithstanding, the shipping situation is still critical, and the submarine alone has made it so. There is no real remedy for underwater attack except to defeat the power which employs it. This the United Nations are attempting to do with aerial bombardment of Germany. More U-boats have been destroyed in one night's bombing of the factories at Augsburg and the base at St. Nazaire than naval measures have accounted for in many months.

We shall win the war in the end; not immediately,

but when the gigantic problems of transport have been solved and the neglect of air power remedied. If our strategists can make full use of the potentialities of the cargo-carrying plane, the submarine may suddenly cease to be the threat it is today. Toward that use every one of us should bend his influence and his thought.

What the citizen should know above all about submarine warfare is that the spirit of the men who are pitting their lives against it is superb. Let every American remember that these men deserve far more cooperation than they are getting from the people ashore.

BIBLIOGRAPHY

HISTORICAL

CABLE, F. T. *Birth and Development of the American Submarine.* New York & London: Harper & Bros., 1924.

COREY, HERBERT. *Submarine; the Autobiography of Simon Lake.* New York & London: Appleton-Century Co., 1938.

JACKSON, G. G. *The Romance of the Submarine.* London: S. Low, Marston & Co., Ltd. [1930?]

PARSONS, W. B. *Robert Fulton and the Submarine.* New York: Columbia University Press, 1922.

WORLD WAR I

FESSENDEN, HELEN M. *Fessenden, Builder of Tomorrows.* New York: Coward-McCann, 1940.

GIBSON, R. H., and PRENDERGAST, MAURICE. *The German Submarine War, 1914–1918.* London: Constable & Co., Ltd., 1931.

GLEAVES, VICE ADMIRAL ALBERT, U.S.N. *History of the Transport Service.* New York: Geo. H. Doran, 1921.

HOUSTON, DAVID F. *Eight Years with Wilson's Cabinet.* Garden City, New York: Doubleday, Page & Co., 1926.

MASTERS, DAVID. *The Submarine War.* New York: Henry Holt & Co., 1935.

MILLIS, WALTER. *Road to War.* Boston & New York: Houghton Mifflin Co., 1935.

SIMS, REAR ADMIRAL WILLIAM S., U.S.N., in collaboration with BURTON J. HENDRICK. *Victory at Sea.* Garden City, New York: Doubleday, Page & Co., 1920.

TIRPITZ, A. P. F. VON. *My Memoirs.* New York: Dodd, Mead & Co., 1919.

SUBMARINE RESCUE

BARROWS, NAT A. *Blow All Ballast! The Story of the Squalus.* New York: Dodd, Mead & Co., 1940.

ELLSBERG, COMMANDER EDWARD, U.S.N. *On the Bottom.* New York: Literary Guild of America, Inc., 1929.

WORLD WAR II

SEVERSKY, ALEXANDER P. DE. *Victory Through Air Power.* New York: Simon & Schuster, 1942.

INDEX